Called Home

The Dartmoor Tin Miner 1860-1940

Called Home

The Dartmoor Tin Miner 1860-1940

Photographs & Memory

by

Tom Greeves

TWELVEHEADS PRESS

TRURO 2016

FRONT COVER: Miners outside Golden Dagger Mine adit. *Chapman & Son* 11937

BACK COVER: Miners' Bunk House and Mine Captain's House, Vitifer Mine, about 1910.

Chapman & Son 11954 (detail)

TWELVEHEADS PRESS

First published 2016 by Twelveheads Press

ISBN 978 0 906294 87 1

British Library Cataloguing-in-Publication Data.

A catalogue record for this book is available from the British Library.

Typeset in Garamond

Printed by Short Run Press Ltd, Exeter

Contents

UNITS OF MEASUREMENT

Units of measurement and money used in this book are those which were concurrent with events described. They may be converted as follows:

Money: £1 = 20 shillings (s) = 100 pence (p)
             1 shilling (s) = 12 pence (d) = 5 pence (p)

Length: 1 mile = 1,760 yards = 1.6093 kilometres
           1 yard = 3 feet = 36 inches = 0.9144 metres

Depth: 1 fathom = 6 feet

LIST OF FIGURES

All are from the author's collection unless otherwise stated. The titles are modern descriptions and not necessarily the same as those on original photographs.

ACKNOWLEDGEMENTS

Research for *Called Home – the Dartmoor Tin Miner 1860-1940: Photographs & Memory* has been generously supported by Neil Mercer of Enigma Solicitors of Plymouth, to whom the author is most grateful.

The following have made this book possible through conversation, permission to use (or loan of) images, technical help and support in many different ways. To all of them I am deeply indebted: Graham Amhof, John Anderson, George Austin, Irene Bailey, Bessie Beer, Elsie Bellamy, Reginald Bellamy, William Bennett, Mrs Bents, Eric Blatchford, William John Bowhay, Beatrice Brook, Malcolm Brook, Justin Brooke, Mrs Burley, Mrs Chaffe, Nigel Chaffers-Heard, Chris Chapman, Ann Chiswell, Elsie Chudley, Frank Chudley, Emily Coaker, Frank Coaker, David Cooper, Marjorie Cooper, Bob Cowan, James Crowden, Pat & Joyce Dennis, Azook Digitising, Walter Dodd, David Edgcombe, Jim Endacott, Agnes Evely, Fred Evely, William Flewin, John & Vivien Forster, Keith Fox, Charles & Joan French, Sidney French, John Gale, Barry Gamble, Cliff Goss, Felicity Greeves, Patrick & Sheila Greeves, A.J.Grose, Alfred Grose, Alfred Truscott Grose, Betsy Grose, Garth Grose, William Grose, Gordon Hambley, John Hamlyn senior, John Hamlyn junior, Deborah Hannaford, Peter Hannaford, George Hellier, Charles Hill, Chris Hill, Tom Hill, Frank Hodge, Robin Hood, Marion Howard, David Hurn, Lilian Jones, Chris Kelland, Wendy Lamble, Annie Leaman, Jan Leaman, Brian Le Messurier, June Lock, Algy May, Neil Mercer, Pat Milton, Henrietta Morgan, Audrey Mortimore, Winnie Murch, Phil Newman, Geoff Old, Colin Olver, John Olver, Amy Osborn, John Osborn, Polly Osborn, George Robertson Owen, Mrs Page, Neil Parkhouse, Janet Parsons, Michael Perriam, Richard Perryman, Roy Petherick, Miss J. Pope, Gertrude Prew, Tom Pridmore, Martin Radford, John Rawlins, Doreen Richards, Peter Richardson, Robert Savery, Sylvia Sayer, Brenda Short, Mr & Mrs Sinclair, Annie Sleep, Donald Smith, Martin Spiller, Elisabeth Stanbrook, Rick Stewart, Studio Canal Ltd, Sydney Taylor, Garfield Thomas, Simon Timms, Torquay Museum, Harry Trude, Ernest Tucker, Blanch and Alfred Wannacott, Alex Warne, Claude Warne, Fernley Warne (Modbury), Fernley Warne (Postbridge), Frank Warne, Gilbert Warne, Louise Warne, Reginald Warne, Claude Warren, William Warren, Emmie Webb, Eva Webb, Tom Webb, Frank Webber, Irene Mary Wellington, Ivan Westcott, Ethel White, Nellie White, Reg White, Frank Williams, Kenneth Williams, Helen Wilson, William Withycombe, Stephen Woods, Ernest Worth.

My wife Elisabeth deserves special thanks for support, help and tolerance. Many thanks too to Alan Kittridge of Twelveheads Press for his skilful design and editing.

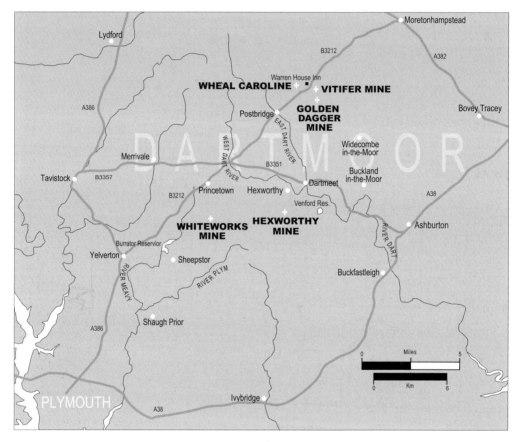

1. Location map of mine locations

INTRODUCTION

Thirty years have now passed since I prepared the first edition of my book *Tin Mines & Miners of Dartmoor – A Photographic Record* (Devon Books, 1986) for publication. In that time I have been fortunate enough to track down previously unknown photographs and information, and this newly written and expanded book is the result.

The book has a new title. 'Called Home' is special to me, as it is a phrase used by several Dartmoor people I spoke to, recollecting the miners who appeared in photographs. 'I can't call 'e home!' was said in frustration at not being able to remember immediately who a particular individual was. It is such an evocative saying, expressing the desire to bring that person back to their familiar world. Of course, for the tin miners, Dartmoor was home, as indeed were some of the mines themselves, besides being places of work and livelihood. My hope is that through this book I have managed to call many of these people home, and have illustrated, through word and image, their proper place in the wonderful human story of Dartmoor.

I have kept my focus on three moorland mines operating during the last days of tinworking c.1900-c.1930. There were several other important and interesting tin mines on the fringes of Dartmoor also working during the early years of the twentieth century – East Vitifer (North Bovey), Devon United (Peter Tavy), Kit (Sheepstor), Owlacombe (Ashburton), Wheal Friendship (Mary Tavy), Wheal Jewell (Mary Tavy) - for most of which some photographic evidence survives. But these, and the tin-producing mines of the Tamar Valley, as well as the works on and around Kester Brook near Ashburton in the 1970s, are on private land and deserve separate treatment. The moorland mines covered here – Hexworthy, Vitifer and Golden Dagger (Fig. 1) – have no restriction on access and so are ideally suited for exploration and interpretation by any interested person. Between them they also have the finest photographic and oral record that has survived.

These mines were the inheritors of an ancient industry. Tin beads of about 1700 BC have been found in a prehistoric cist grave at Whitehorse Hill on northern Dartmoor.[1] It is almost inconceivable that these were not made of Dartmoor stream tin, and it is to be hoped that isotopic proof will one day confirm this. We also now know, through sediments in old river channels[2] and through metallic residues in peat bogs[3] that there was tinworking and tin smelting taking place on Dartmoor in the first millennium AD. The documentary story begins in the twelfth century, and is continuous since then, recording periods of significant prosperity around AD 1300 and from about 1450-1600.[4] In about 1600 tinworking in Devon was still considered to be more important than maritime activity.[5] In the mid-nineteenth century about fifty tin mines were producing tin within the county. In 2015 Wolf Minerals began production at a new mine at Drakelands (Hemerdon) on the edge of Dartmoor and 1,000 tonnes of tin concentrate are expected to be produced annually during the life of the mine (which is primarily extracting tungsten).

Before turning to the individual mines in detail, three images deserve to be presented. The first (Fig. 2) is a remarkable discovery of a photograph of tin miners and a waterwheel at Vitifer Mine taken in the early 1860s by an Exeter lithographer and photographer, William Spreat (born 1816). It is by far the earliest known contemporary image of a working Dartmoor tin mine. The original was published as a stereoview i.e. with two almost identical images stuck on a card side by side. These could then be viewed through a stereoscope which created the illusion of a single image in three dimensions.

The photograph, which I have described elsewhere[6] shows a group of sixteen Dartmoor tin miners (men and boys) at Vitifer Mine, posed beside a large cast iron waterwheel. The background view is of the Redwater valley looking southwards towards Challacombe Down. In the middle distance on the left are sheds which are precursors of the later main Vitifer Mine dressing floor (see Figs 62-66). Everywhere in the valley is bare ground turned over by the tinners. This was the peak period of Birch Tor & Vitifer Mine – 150 persons were employed above and below ground in 1863.[7]

The photograph predates by about twenty-five years the next earliest image of mining machinery on moorland Dartmoor (Fig. 3), and about forty years earlier than any previously confirmed image of miners themselves. It is also the first known photograph of this particular waterwheel.

The location can be precisely identified at SX 68178090. The heather-covered heap of spoil on which the group is positioned, and the heap in the foreground, both still exist exactly as shown. The stone-lined pit for the waterwheel is still visible and measures internally 13m x 1.5m (43ft x 5ft).[8] The wheel is likely to have been used for pumping Dunstan's Shaft on the Old Vitifer Lode (see Fig. 52), which was named after Capt. Richard Dunstan. He was one of two captains on the mine from at least

the mid-1840s to the early 1850s.[9] He was a Cornishman, born in Bodmin in about 1807.[10] Early in 1850 he was accused of encouraging a brawl among miners at the nearby New House Inn (i.e. Warren House), which he hotly denied.[11] He was concerned at the lack of accommodation provided for the miners, and resigned after expressing dissatisfaction with the actions of the directors in diverting money away from this.[12]

Dunstan's shaft was being sunk in 1848 and eventually reached a depth of at least 40 fathoms (240ft).[13] When it reached the Old Vitifer Lode great festivities were held on the mine, which was declared to be 'on the brink of becoming the richest in Europe'.[14]

The wheel was probably also used for stamping (i.e. crushing) ore. The photograph confirms neither of these functions, and it may be that the wheel was newly installed and still had additions to be made, or was being refurbished.

2. Waterwheel and miners by Dunstan's Shaft, Vitifer Mine, early 1860s. *W. Spreat, John Anderson collection*

It is exceptional for a photograph of this era to show a posed group of working people. Two underground miners are distinctly shown – fourth and fifth from the left in the front row are men with underground clothes and hard hats, each with a lump of clay and a candle stuck on it. The righthand man has tallow candles slung round his neck. A third, younger, man, second from right in the front row, is also wearing underground clothes and is holding his hat. He appears to be wearing a close-fitting skullcap. The attire of these underground miners looks very similar to that of fifty years later in the early 1900s (see, for example, Figs 59 and 67). The remaining adult men and boys look distinctly more 'old-fashioned' in their dress, with braces holding up their trousers which appear to have a front flap, and waistcoats. All these men, and quite possibly all of the boys, will have been born in the first half of the nineteenth century.

Fig. 3 shows an abandoned stamps waterwheel at Whiteworks Mine, near Princetown taken by Robert Burnard, a manufacturer of artificial manure, who took up photography in about 1888, when aged forty. This wheel is likely to have been one recorded as 30ft in diameter and bought by the mine in 1869. It was the higher of two stamps wheels which were remembered by Ernest Worth of Peat Cot as being 'sunk into the ground like a ship in water'.[15] By the time this photograph was taken, the wheel was abandoned, with its stamps axle lying out of position. But the sixteen

3. Stamps
waterwheel at
Whiteworks Mine,
1 June 1889.
R. Burnard

stamps were still in position – in four sets of four, their wooden 'lifters'
are clearly visible. A raised timber structure leading to the back of the
wheel is probably a tramroad for taking ore to feed under the stamps.
Whiteworks was one of Dartmoor's largest moorland tin mines and
operated intermittently, on the site of much earlier workings, from about
1786 until about 1914.[16]

Fig. 4 is of lesser quality but still significant, as it is the only known
photograph of a waterwheel at a mine called Wheal Caroline, which was
located about 500m west of the Warren House Inn, and close to Vitifer
Mine. The wheel itself was sited in a gully at SX 688808 but powered
pumping rods which were led up the hill to the east for some 250m to
drain a shaft at SX 67098095, close to the top of Water Hill. The mine
was working from at least the 1820s to the 1860s.[17] The wheel was
removed in about 1909, the occasion being remembered by Annie Sleep
of Postbridge because a young man was killed on the same day, in an
unconnected accident on Merripit Hill, involving a horse and cart.[18]

5. Ernest, Elsie and Mabel Worth of Peat Cot, 21 December 1972. *T. Greeves*

People and Process

My latent interest in Dartmoor tin mining was stimulated by the Plymouth Branch of the Devonshire Association in the late 1960s, whose members embarked on a study of Ailsborough (Eylesbarrow) tin mine in Sheepstor parish. I joined the team and carried out fieldwork and documentary research in Devon, Cornwall and London. I also began talking to the older generation of Dartmoor people, such as the Worth family of Peat Cot (Fig. 5) who had direct experience or memory of the last days of tin mining from the late nineteenth century onwards. My first meeting with a former tin miner was in 1969 when I met Harry Trude (Figs 6 & 7) who had worked on the surface at Vitifer and Golden Dagger

6. Harry and Lilian Trude at Sunnymead, Postbridge, Summer 1969. *T. Greeves*

after the First World War. A breakthrough came in August 1970 when Annie Sleep (Fig. 8) of Postbridge showed me two high quality photographs (on postcards) predating the First World War (Figs 100 & 103) of miners at Golden Dagger Mine. These are two of a carefully conceived series of record images of Birch Tor & Vitifer and Golden Dagger mines taken by Chapman & Son, commercial photographers of Dawlish. Sixteen postcard images in a series numbered 11937-11960 have now been traced. If all serial numbers were used, perhaps two dozen were produced originally.[19] It is fascinating to speculate why these were taken, presumably at the request of mining personnel. There may be a connection with Captain William Bennetts who was at

8. Miss Annie Sleep of Fairholm, Postbridge, 21 March 1972. *T. Greeves*

10. William Flewin at Golden Dagger Mine, I July 1996. *T. Greeves*

7. Harry Trude at Golden Dagger Mine, 22 September 1971. *T. Greeves*

9.
George Austin of Moretonhampstead, 1982.
Chris Chapman

Vitifer from about 1907,[20] and who was the son of the well-known Cornish mine photographer, William John Bennetts of Camborne.

It was not until February 1974 that I met a man who had worked underground on moorland Dartmoor tin mines. This was Sidney French (1889-1976), whose family farmed at Middle Merripit, Postbridge, but who worked at all three mines (Hexworthy, Vitifer and Golden Dagger) between 1903-1913.

George Austin (Fig. 9) and William (Bill) Flewin (Fig. 10) were among those I met who had experience of Golden Dagger Mine in the 1920s. But as early as October 1970 I had received a letter (Fig. 11) from Donald Smith (1907-1993) who was employed at Golden Dagger Mine from 1925 and who was manager of the mine 1927-1930. In 1983 I was able to take him back to Golden Dagger Mine (Fig. 12) and also visited him at his home in Portslade (Fig. 13). His recollections and the remarkable photographic record he made of the mine are unique and of exceptional value.

But perhaps even more surprising was the contact I established with Cornish-born William Grose (1886-1994), thanks to meeting relatives of

11. Letter (detail) from Donald Smith, 5 October 1970

12. Donald Smith by round buddle, Golden Dagger Mine, 26 May 1983. *T. Greeves*

his in Ashburton in the early 1970s, who told me of his existence in Montana, USA. His knowledge of Dartmoor mining stretched back to the 1890s when he visited his grandparents in Ilsington, but his particular

13. Donald Smith in his workshop at 5 Sharpthorne Crescent, Portslade, Brighton, 4 September 1988. *T. Greeves*

experience which enthralled me was that, as a teenager, he lived with his parents and siblings on Hexworthy Mine for several years around 1900, and was actually employed there. His father, Ambrose Grose, was manager of the mine. My first letter from him was dated 1 December 1974 when he was already aged eighty-eight (Fig. 14). I had stirred memories of more than seventy years previously and William commented, 'I can scarcely write about it'.[21] But a wonderful correspondence ensued (Fig. 15) – one letter in 1976 was of no less than 12½ pages, each 9 in x 6 in and of 29 neatly written

14. Letter (detail) from William Grose, 1 December 1974.

> 822 Cottonwood Street
> Missoula
> Montana 59801
> U.S.A.
> Dear Mr Greeves -   December 1st 1974
>   I received your letter of Sept. 15, and have read & re-read it with great interest. The delay in answering is due to the fact that I had a rather serious operation this spring & hasnt been able to work up much energy since, also I was 86 years old in November. However I am fairly well now except for old aches & pains am in good health, likewise Mrs Grose for which we are thankful.
>   It is true I can answer most of the questions you ask. I knew Atlas mine at Ilsington well, played around there as a child, & later after it was shut down. My Grandfather Wm. A. Grose was manager, my Father & his brothers worked there. I lived at Heeworthy several years with my Father & Mother & knew the "layout" & operation of both Atlas & Heeworthy, (Atlas 1890-1894) (Heeworthy 1898-1904). also Owlacombe (1904 to 1908), also its complete layout during that time, many who worked there in all of them, in fact I am I believe the only one left who can, a fact which has startled me.
>   I have been busy with many things this fall, & have slowed up a lot, but your letter has intrigued me. I am unable to give you the above in detail in this letter but I will later. I will

lines. In another letter (6 November 1977) he wrote, '…it all comes back to me & I may say with considerable emotion. Your questions in your letters were the means of bringing back memories. I have lived those days over again'.[22]

William was apprenticed as an engineer at Willcocks & Son in Buckfastleigh from 1903-1907. From 1908-1921 he worked as an engineer for Holman's in Camborne, and then emigrated to the USA. I had the good fortune of being able to make visits to him and his wife

15. Letter (detail) from William Grose, 11 June 1976.

> Heeworthy picture   (on the horizon)
> I can identify it all Tom, The building at the left the longest is where we lived, a 4 roomed house & the mine office, the ... to the right the dry, where left chimneys were ours, then a division & to the right the dry, where the miners dried their went underground clothes, the third chimney was from the drying fire, then the smaller building on the end the blacksmith's shop. Upstairs over the dry was a dormitory with 12 or 14 beds where the men slept who stayed all week, Monday to Saturday noon, that is they that lived too far away to commute. The mine furthest to the right was where they lived & had their meals, this one was built of wood & covered with galvanized iron, was known as the iron house. The water wheel was 45 feet in diameter, & I believe 5 or 6 feet wide, the Cornish Stamps at the right, At the face the faint outline of the old Cornish Stamps Father installed. ... the upright rods, of the California Stamps. The ... with the path leading down was where the tram road came with the ore from the shaft, from there on to the back of the stamps was a short viaduct, the small house was where the men had their lunches, that little path I have come down many times,

23

16. William and Bessie Grose at 522 Cottonwood Street, Missoula, Montana USA, August 1981. *T. Greeves*

Bessie in America in 1981 and 1986 (Figs 16-18), on the second of which I was able to reunite him with his christening mug which had been kept safe by his niece Joyce Dennis (née Grose) of Ashburton. His irrepressible interest, and astonishing longevity, living nearly to 108, enabled him to contribute a unique record of Dartmoor mining and miners. On 4 June 1996 his son Alfred (1924-2000) travelled for the first time to Hexworthy Mine, and stood on the ruins of the Engine House by Low's Shaft, from which he released some of his father's ashes, in an unforgettable moment of miraculously gentle spontaneity and poetic beauty. The cloud of ash was caught by the breeze and drifted gently towards the Mine House and great wheelpit opposite Dry Lake. William Grose was undoubtedly called home that day. Happily, I still remain in contact with his grandchildren.

BELOW LEFT:
17. William Grose with christening mug, 14 October 1986. *T. Greeves*

BELOW RIGHT:
18. William Grose, aged 100, at 522 Cottonwood Street, Missoula, Montana, USA, 15 October 1986. *T. Greeves*

HEXWORTHY MINE

Hexworthy tin mine, often known as Hensroost (pronounced 'Insroost' locally) is entirely on open moorland, at about 1,300 ft (400m) above sea level, near the head of the O (or Wo) Brook which itself is a tributary of the West Dart river (Fig. 19). Like most Dartmoor tin mines, tinworking in the area was of ancient origin. Dry Lake, a tributary of the O Brook and marking the boundary of the Forest of Dartmoor, is documented as a tinwork in AD 1240 when it was known as 'la Dryeworke'.[23] Several sixteenth and seventeenth-century tinworks are mentioned in the area within either Lydford parish (which included the Forest of Dartmoor) and neighbouring Holne.[24] The mine complex itself

19. Map of Hexworthy Mine, based on OS 2nd edn 6-inch, 1906, Sheet 107SE (not to scale).

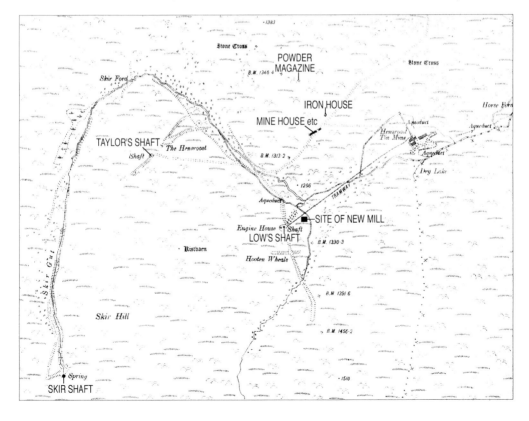

20. Frederick Pine Theophilus Struben (from Macdonald, n.d., frontispiece).

has two main areas of working – at Hensroost (SX 651711) and Hooten Wheals (SX 656708). Both of these comprise large scale gullies created by opencast linear workings, probably of medieval origin, following lodes to a depth of 60-100ft, with shafts sunk even deeper. The tinners called such workings beamworks. The mine itself is not documented until the mid-nineteenth century,[25] and little is known of activity until the late 1880s and 1890s when the well-known firm of John Taylor & Sons invested in it. There were nearly sixty employees in 1891 but a mine sale on 5 December 1895 marked a temporary end of activity. However, it was soon revived under new leases granted to Edward Herbert Bayldon of Dawlish, sometimes jointly with Frederick Pine Theophilus Struben (1851-1931) (Fig. 20) of Kya Lami, Haldon Road, Torquay.[26] The latter was an unlikely benefactor of Hexworthy Mine. He and his brother Harry (Henrik Wilhelm) were among the first discoverers of a gold reef on the Rand in South Africa,[27] which brought them considerable wealth. In the late nineteenth century, when he was still in his forties, he moved to England. Among his purchases was Spitchwick Manor in the parish of Widecombe-in-the-Moor, allegedly for £25,000[28] and, soon afterwards, with Edward Herbert Bayldon, he decided to invest money in Hexworthy Mine for which he had obtained a one-year licence for the sett from 17 January 1897 and for two years from 17 January 1898, from the Duchy of Cornwall.[29]

William Grose had the task of showing his son Leicester Frederick Struben (1893-1916) round the mine when he and his father rode up to the mine one day on 'high class horses' and 'perfectly attired in riding clothes'. Leicester spoke 'in the language of the young aristocrat and turned out to be a very agreeable young gentleman'.[30] Leicester was reported missing when flying over enemy lines on 16 November 1916[31], and there is a memorial to him in Leusdon church. Frederick Struben died in 1931 and is buried in the graveyard at Leusdon.

Edward Herbert Bayldon (1855-1912) of Oaklands, Dawlish who joined with Frederick Struben to acquire leases of the mine in the late 1890s, obtained a 21-year lease of Hensroost from the Duchy of Cornwall from 17 January 1900. In the census of 1901 he is described as 'mine owner'; in 1881 he had been a stockbroker living in Kensington, London. He had previously had an interest in iron mines at Brixham where both William Grose senior and his son Pharaoh worked.[32] He was later to develop a tin mine at Stormsdown (Owlacombe) and also acquired Wheal Friendship at Mary Tavy.[33]

The involvement of Bayldon and Struben includes the period of about five years (1898-1903) remembered by William Ambrose Grose who noted that at this time the mine was not run by a company, but was 'owned and financed by one Gentleman Mr Bayldon and he was a very conservative gentleman, not the kind of man it would be easy to approach for information'.[34] This perhaps explains why no record of this phase of activity has yet been traced in official business records.

William Grose stated that there 'were more improvements made during our sojourn there than at any previous time, of that I am certain because I saw the old or obsolete methods scrapped & new ones & ideas installed'.[35] He recalled that in 1900 some 7 tons of tin from Hexworthy were sold at the tin ticketings in Redruth for the then record price of £95 5s per ton.[36]

It was Mr Bayldon who offered Ambrose John Grose (1866-1951) (Fig. 21) the managership of Hexworthy Mine. Ambrose was then in his early thirties. He was born into a mining family (his parents were William and Emily Grose) at Constantine in Cornwall and married Jessica (Jessie) Bunney (1868-1946) there on 6 June 1886. She was born in St Stephen-in-Brannel. Their first child, William Ambrose, was born on 8 November of that year. Ambrose began work at Hexworthy in 1898 and created a home there for his wife and three children. He was described as 'a real Cornishman with a great sense of humour'. He was considerably experienced and widely travelled as a mining man by then, having worked in Michigan, USA for the Buffalo Mining Company and Queen Iron Mining Co. in the earlier 1890s – while there he attended evening schools in mechanical subjects. He also worked in India, at the Balaghat Nundadrug Gold Mine, Coramandal and at the Kolar Gold Fields, Ooregum, Mysore, in Karnataka State in which John Taylor & Sons had an interest.[37] In June and July 1898 he was Captain of a gold mine in west Africa – the

21. Ambrose John Grose about 1900. *Edwin Kelly Studio*

22. William
Ambrose Grose
about 1900.
B. Julyan, St Austell

Wassau (Gold Coast) Mining Co. Ltd at Adjah Bippo – but the climate 'proved too much for him' and he was invalided back to Britain with fever. Soon afterwards he was appointed manager at Hexworthy Mine.[38] Edward Mogridge, an elderly caretaker, was living on the mine at the time, and Ambrose had some difficulty persuading him to move to Tavistock to enable his (Ambrose's) wife and family to move into the building.[39] Mogridge was a gentleman of Moretonhampstead who, with others, had held leases of the mine from 1889-1896.[40]

William described his father as 'more of a surface man, although he did understand minerals and mining procedure & production'.[41] He 'was a skilled man around machinery, engines, pumps etc' and had learnt a great deal in North America.[42] Ambrose was 'a good penman & wrote a very neat hand, so did Mother. I used to marvel at the Cost Sheets he made out. They were always neat and well done.' [43] Ambrose was a freemason, and also had great empathy with animals who would follow him. Birds would also come to him when he whistled.[44]

We have to thank William Ambrose Grose (Fig. 22) for his vivid recollections of life on Hexworthy Mine in the years around 1900. He was there at the time of the census in April 1901 when he was described as

23. Ivy Cottage, St Stephen, Cornwall, birthplace of William A. Grose on 8 November 1886. *Photographer not known*

'Attending School'. This was at St Stephen-in-Brannel in the clayworking district of Cornwall where he lived in the family home of Ivy Cottage (Fig. 23), where he himself was born. He had actually first visited Dartmoor from about 1890, staying with his grandparents William and Emily Grose at Lewthorn Cross, Ilsington. William senior was manager of adjoining Atlas tin mine where Ambrose worked. But as an older schoolchild William junior would spend holidays at Hexworthy Mine from

1899. In January 1901 he remembers his schoolmaster announcing the death of Queen Victoria, but by the spring of that year had left school and was put on the payroll at Hexworthy Mine. He was at the mine in September 1901 when he read in the *Western Morning News* of the assassination of President Mckinley of the USA.[45]

24. Pumping and stamps waterwheel opposite Dry Lake about 1905, from E (approx). *Photographer not known*

Dominating Fig. 24 is a very large (45ft/13.7m x 5ft/1.5m) waterwheel and launder opposite Dry Lake – a magnificent sight on moorland Dartmoor. I have not yet traced an original print but was sent this good copy as long ago as 1974 by Martin Radford of Malvern. Faint outlines on the horizon are of the key mine buildings, and so far this is the only known photograph of them when intact.

The family home is visible as the lefthand building on the horizon in Fig. 24. William commented, '…there was something about the place. I don't know what it was, but I loved it. Then there were that superb couple, my Father & Mother, handsome, graceful, full of good humour, witty, & full of love and understanding' (Fig. 25).[46] The two lefthand chimneys belonged to the family rooms. William had two younger siblings – Alfred Truscott and Mona ('Queenie'), both also born at St Stephen in Cornwall. At the time of the census in April 1901 the whole

25. Ambrose and
Jessie Grose in
Ashburton, 1930s.
ex Garth Grose

family was at Hexworthy Mine, with Alfred aged 2 and Mona just 1. It was a four-roomed dwelling – 'substantially built' and 'comfortable'. There was no back door, but Ambrose added a porch at the front.[47] Downstairs on the left was the mine office, panelled with long strips of varnished wood, and complete with desk, table and fireplace, and three windows. It doubled as a sitting-room. A pair of assayer's scales (for weighing tin samples) were found there when the Groses moved in. The other room was the kitchen and family 'living room'. Upstairs were two bedrooms – one for the Grose parents, one for the children. There were windows on the back of the house. Fowls, three geese and some ducks were kept. Groceries were delivered on Tuesday evenings by Bolt's of Princetown, Jessie Grose having sent an order via the postman on the previous Saturday. The house was once unexpectedly invaded by cockroaches which had almost certainly arrived in the sacks of barley for the ducks! Post was delivered to the mine by Edward Lee from Princetown who called daily on foot via Tor Royal and Sherberton,[48] and also sometimes by Fred Chudley of Gobbett before going to school.[49]

William had many domestic duties as well those on the mine. Water for washing came from a bog above the house. Drinking water came from a spring below the house, which he collected twice daily in two cans hung from an iron hoop.[50] He was sent to Hexworthy daily (except Sundays) to fetch milk, butter, eggs and cream. The Cleave children at the Forest Inn 'weren't very clean' and William saw one of the daughters, Nina, take the spoon with which the cream was served, out of a drawer and then scratch her back with it. He told his mother who accompanied him on one occasion and witnessed it herself, and forbade him to go there again,[51] so he had to make a significantly longer journey to Sherberton Farm instead (seen in the background of Fig. 27), past the home of the Chudley family at Gobbett Mine cottages and then often back via Hexworthy to perhaps hand mail to Edward Lee who would have his lunch at the Forest Inn before setting off back to Princetown on foot. Jim Chudley (Fig. 26) (1860-c.1951) did surface work on the mine as 'pithead man and general help' earning £1 per week.[52] He also carried bedding from the miners' Dry on his back every week from the mine to Gobbett (Fig. 27) for his wife to wash. Mrs Grose took care of the family laundry.[53] Born at Whitestone near Exeter, he worked as a farm labourer at Dunsford/ Drewsteignton but moved to Gobbett in 1890 to earn more money at the mine. He had a large family. His daughter Rose, who was born at Gobbett during the great blizzard of March 1891,[54] used to help Jessie Grose by looking after Alfred and Queenie, and she and her sister Annie were often up at the house, sometimes 'purely for

26. James Chudley, tin mine labourer, of Gobbett and Swincombe, in 1938.
Frank Chudley

company' as it could be lonely for Jessie Grose there.[55] Jim Chudley's sons Frederick (Fred) (born c. 1887) and William (Bill) (1884-1953) were both employed as 'tin mine labourers' on the dressing floors at Hexworthy Mine.[56] In 1903 they both left the area to become locomotive firemen on the London & South Western Railway at Nine Elms and Guildford respectively.[57] Fred was particularly keen on machinery and made a model of tin stamps at Gobbett[58] which, sadly, was vandalised. William commented that 'they were a fine family and highly respected'.[59]

William's hair, and that of some of the miners, was cut by Tom Peters of Jordan Street, Buckfastleigh, who was born in Cornwall. William paid him 2d.[60]

27. Gobbett Cottages, home of Chudley family c.1890-1913.
Photographer not known

William was put on the payroll of the mine at the age of 14½, as errand boy. On 29 May 1903, aged 16½ he was enrolled on a 4½-year apprenticeship as a 'fitter and turner' at the ironfounding and engineering firm of Willcocks & Son of the Dial Foundry in Buckfastleigh. He was taught by Abraham Knott.[61] He was unpaid until 8 November 1903 (his 17th birthday) but for the year following received two shillings per week. From November 1904 he got three shillings, from November 1905 five shillings, and from November 1906 six shillings per week, until his twenty-first birthday on 8 November 1907.[62]

The Bayldons would visit every now and then during the summer. They would have lunch in the sitting room with the door closed, leaving part of a bottle of good wine when they left. 'On one of their early visits Mrs Bayldon remarking on the loneliness of the place said "Do you & your young son like to read?", which we did and after that they brought many magazines and books, & it was from these books the Bayldons brought that I made my first acquaintance with R. L. Stevenson, Rudyard Kipling, Joseph Conrad, A. Conan Doyle & Jules Verne [and] many others that started me on an avid love of good literature'.[63] Mr Barrington, the Duchy Land Steward, also visited every now and then.[64]

Early November was special to William as it included Guy Fawkes Day (5th) and his birthday (8th). One year, when Guy Fawkes Day fell at a weekend, his father had forgotten to buy the usual fireworks when in Ashburton collecting the men's wages, but he had an idea.

> 'A new barrel of grease had arrived [and] the old barrel still had a lot of old dried grease adhering to the inside. He said when it gets dark go over & roll the old barrel down the slope a little way, fill it with shavings & scrap wood from the carpenters shop & I will come down and we will have a bonfire. It was Saturday and no one there but us, & a black overcast November night. I got a lantern and did as he said & we certainly had a bonfire – the flames must have been 20 feet high. I remember saying to Father, "Can anybody see this but us?" There could not have been. Behind us was Down Ridge, in front the hill, beyond which was Scoriton, the rest entirely out of view, each side. No one would be out on the moor that black November night. The nearest people would be at the Forest Inn, 1½ miles away, over the hill. I remember looking back at the house. Mother was looking out of the bedroom window. Never a Guy Fawkes day has passed since then when I haven't lived it all over again'.[65]

The righthand chimney of the lefthand building in Fig. 24 was for the 'Dry' where the miners' underground clothes were dried. There were windows at the back. The Dry itself was on the ground floor and consisted of a long steel tube about two-thirds full of water, with a firebox at one end. Gases passed underneath its entire length. Wet clothes were draped over it and on racks overhead. William described improvements made by his father Ambrose: 'It was not really a 'boiler' but a water heater, about 12 feet long and 3ft 6in or 4 feet in diameter. Father conceived the idea of putting a tube down through the middle of it and arrange for the fire and gases to go through the tube and not under the boiler, thus this inner tube would be entirely surrounded by water and would heat faster. Care had to be taken, and was, that evaporation would be faster and an adequate vent was installed and the water level above the tube inspected which was my job. It had to be not less than six inches above the tube.'

Alterations were carried out in the summer so that, it was hoped, the clothes could be dried naturally, but inevitably some days it was rainy or cool and 'often the miners went underground with wet clothes'. William remembered that most took it in good humour, knowing things would improve when the work was completed, but Bill Blackmore, a 'crusty old miner' from Jordan Street, Buckfastleigh, complained bitterly: 'One day going underground in wet clothes he said (I heard him say it), "What the hell are things coming to? If my old woman knowed that I was going to work in wet clothes like this, er'd piss 'erself"'.[66]

Above the Dry was a dormitory with twelve or fourteen beds in two rows, where the men slept who stayed for the week from Monday to Saturday midday. It dates at least from the 1890s as an auction of materials on 5 December 1895 had included '20 iron beds, with mattresses, palliases, pillows. Sheets, blankets and counterpanes'.[67]

Attached to the righthand end of the Dry was a single-storey structure with a chimney. This was the Blacksmith's Shop where James (Jim) Chapman of Jordan Street, Buckfastleigh worked. He was aged fifty-six at the time of the census of 1901 and had been born in Cornwall (St Columb), as had his wife and their eight children (St Wenn). Much of his time was spent sharpening drills for the underground miners. He was always smoking a clay pipe. He would light it with a poker from the fire and seemed to spend 'more time filling and lighting it than working'! His son Philip worked with him[68] – it was he who was thought to have destroyed the model stamps made by Fred Chudley at Gobbett.

The small 'middle' building on the horizon was the Carpenter's Shop at SX 65707113 where old Tommy Johns of Lustleigh (c.1840-1917) worked (Fig. 28). He had a speech defect caused by a

28. Tommy Johns (c. 1840-1917), miner and carpenter, about 1900. *Photographer not known*

hole in the roof of his mouth, and was quite difficult to understand, but was a fine and skilled carpenter, with long experience of working in Dartmoor mines, including Steeperton, Vitifer, Atlas and Owlacombe,[69] although originally a ship's carpenter. He was born in Germoe near Porthleven in Cornwall. His father was alleged to have been 'king' of the smugglers in Penzance.[70] At the end of his working week he would walk to Ashburton or Buckfastleigh from the mine and take the train to Totnes, then to Newton Abbot and then from Newton to Lustleigh.[71]

The righthand building was known as the Iron House at SX 65727118, having a wooden frame covered with galvanized iron. Some men slept here, but it was mostly a place where the miners cooked and ate their meals, or stayed when not working on a shift. A man would be delegated to heat up food for the miners coming off a shift.

About 200 yards beyond the mine buildings, on the open moor at SX 65627130, was the Powder Magazine where dynamite (gelignite), fuses and detonators were stored. Peter Richardson sketched it in about 1935.[72] William Grose described his duties:

> 'I had to deal out to the miners all of these supplies when they changed shifts at 2.00 o'clock & keep an accurate account of them...'[73] 'The building was well built, with a fence around, and gate with lock. The door to the building also had two locked doors. To enter one had to unlock the outer door, then face the inner door, in a space of about two feet, where a man could stand. In that space were two overshoes large enough to put your shoes in – in that way it would not be necessary to remove your shoes. These overshoes were made of some non-flammable material, and put together with copper rivets. Then you could unlock the inner door, step over a wooden barrier or screen and 'clip clop' and take a supply of gelignite. It was very carefully packaged and came in wood boxes about 1 foot square and 3 or 4 feet long. If a fresh box had to be opened, then one had to use the copper wedges, copper hammer, and copper crowbar. The use of these copper tools was to prevent sparks. It was really a relic of the days when gunpowder was used. If any gunpowder was spilled on the floor and a spark from a shoe nail or hammer got to it, the whole building could blow up. These strict regulations were carried on into the use of dynamite, and had to be adhered to, and which I at all times observed. My father came up there sometimes to see that they were, in every detail. He was the one who instructed me in the procedure in the first place'.[74]

Sergeant Crispin from Princetown police station visited the mine each year to check on the dynamite licence.[75] William also recalled that the door had a brass lock and a brass key.[76]

Until the modernisation of 1905-1907, when an electric turbine was installed at Saddle Bridge, the large wheel opposite Dry Lake (Fig. 24) was the primary energy source for the mine, providing power for

stamping (crushing) ore. It was 45ft (13.7m) in diameter and 5ft (1.5m) wide.[77] The pumping rods seen leading out of the photograph to the left were not there in William Grose's day. They were installed in about 1905 and were 'as thick as a jam jar'.[78] The wheel is 'pitchback' – the vertical box-like structure attached to the launder was known as a 'downright hatch' and, by means of a wire, water could be turned off the wheel.[79] On the right of the photograph can be seen the stamps axle which once powered twelve Cornish stamps. On the other side of the wheel are the slim lifters for sixteen Californian stamps – these twisted on each lift and thus spread the wear on the head more evenly. They had been brought from Terras Mine, St Stephen-in-Brannel, in Cornwall, which was then worked by Captain Olver,[80] and were installed by Ambrose Grose, thus replacing the Cornish stamps.[81] Stamps needing more ore were said to be 'hungry'.[82] The stamps fell onto a thick iron die which wore in various ways as did the heads.[83] Significant damage could be done to wheels by ice. Tin dresser John Webb of Powder Mills was injured by falling ice when, with others, he was clearing ice from 'a large water wheel' (almost certainly this one) on 6 January 1908.[84]

Fig. 29 shows the wheel in its moorland setting seen from the west in a photograph by W. R. Gay dating from about 1910. The massive timber launder is clearly visible. A more substantial shed than that shown in Fig. 24 is visible, as is the very end of the stone leat embankment. Not seen is the long pond or reservoir (crossed by the track leading down to the

29. Waterwheel opposite Dry Lake from W (approx), about 1910.
W. R. Gay

35

wheel) which was used for storing water in summer. The pond took about two hours to fill and provided enough water for the stamps to work for about two hours. In winter the stamps might be going day and night.[85]

William recalled five waterwheels at the mine in his day. The large wheel opposite Dry Lake powered stamps only. Pumping from Low's Shaft was then powered by a smaller wheel 30-35 ft in diameter and 3-4 ft breast, on the lower side of a track at SX 65657088. Iron rods (flat rods) were taken off an 'inside crank near the hillside' and led to the shaft, supported on 'grooved wheels'. The 'outside or opposite crank' went to Taylor's Shaft about half a mile further up the valley, but these rods were disconnected in William's day.[86] The wheel worked continuously seven days a week and was only stopped for repairs or emergencies when the steam pump was used. On moonlit nights, seen from the Mine House, 'the arms of the wheel would flash as they revolved'.[87] At the shaft the rocking mechanism which converted the horizontal motion of the rods to a vertical motion was called a balance bob. The top of it was known as the Bishop's Head.[88] The suction pipe was known as the windbore ('wind' rhymes with 'mind').

A third wheel only 3 or 4 feet in diameter drove 'revolving frames' (an advanced type of round buddle) that treated the crushed ore from the stamps opposite Dry Lake. The frames required very little power. The wheel itself came from Brixham. A fourth wheel, 6 feet in diameter and about 1 ft breast, was made by carpenter Tommy Johns and drove the round buddles. Waterwheels were a peculiarity of a mine carpenter's work, requiring an understanding of circles, segments and arcs of circles.[89] Eight arcs were required for the rims of a 6ft buddle wheel, then cut out [and] 'rabbetted' (i.e. rebated) for the buckets which had to be divided equally for a 6ft circle.[90] The fifth waterwheel, 15ft-20ft in diameter by about 2ft-2ft 6in breast, drove a pulveriser installed by Ambrose Grose a little distance from the bottom of the dressing floors sand burrow to rework the 'waste' sands which he believed to still contain recoverable tin. The wheel, which had iron spokes and rims, with wooden buckets (made by Tommy Johns), and the pulveriser both came from F. Bartle & Sons' foundry at Carn Brea in Cornwall. The pulveriser consisted of a heavy circular iron pan about 3 feet in diameter with 'heavy revolving chilled iron shoes revolving inside and further grinding the sand to a uniform texture or size', followed by further buddling and treatment. This proved profitable and 'worth the expense'.[91] William also recalled an abandoned waterwheel below Taylor's Shaft, about 12 feet in diameter, which he played on. He thought it might have been set in the outflow from an adit.[92] He knew another, flooded, shaft at Skir (approx. SX 64757033), further up the valley, with water flowing out of the top and timbers visible within the shaft.

The dressing floors were under cover in a shed. 'There were three round buddles at the dressing floors and two square. All except one round buddle in a building, wood building I believe. They were below the waterwheel.' There were also two kieves, and a heavy wooden hutch where the tin was stored and kept locked.[93]

The tin dresser was Richard (Dicky) Jones of Jordan Street, Buckfastleigh – a 'fussy old fellow' who had a workforce of eight or nine men and boys. He was aged 55 at the time of the 1901 census. William would be told to 'wipe they shoes' if entering the dressing floors. In hot dry weather it could get very dusty with sand blowing about and William recalls Dicky Jones saying one day, 'Us be stiffled doon yer'[94] – some of these sands are visible in the foreground of Fig. 24. The small hut is where the men could eat or keep their lunches. A photograph was taken of Dicky Jones at the dressing floor by a Miss [?Mrs] Bernard Wishaw and William remembered that it was published in some newspaper or magazine [95] – despite enquiry, this has not yet been traced. Ambrose Grose had a somewhat difficult relationship with Dicky Jones and two of his sons – Robert (Bob), the older, was aged 25 in 1901 and worked as an underground miner; Jack was aged 19 in 1901. At one time Dicky had to leave the mine after writing to Mr Bayldon with complaints, but soon was re-employed. The letter and Mr Bayldon's typewritten comments were pinned to the wall of the Iron House where all miners could see it.[96]

Low's Shaft (SX 65577081) is almost certainly named after Malcolm Low MP (1835-1923) who was Chairman of the Directors of Hexworthy Tin Mine under John Taylor & Sons.[97] He was MP for Grantham from 1886-1892 and happens to be the great-great-grandfather of Prime Minister David Cameron.[98] Taylor's shaft is probably named after John Taylor & Sons.

Both shafts originally had horse-powered whims for hauling. At Low's Shaft the 'horse whim was there when Father went there first – it shocked him to see such a monstrosity and he soon got the steam hoist',[99] which worked perfectly. The horse whim raised and lowered barrel-shaped iron kibbles, which were tipped into tram wagons. The whim operator, Bill Lance of Hexworthy, would shout 'Streak!' as the command for the horse to change direction, forward or back.[100] This is an old Cornish word recorded in Pryce's *Mineralogia Cornubiensis* of 1778.[101]

Ambrose Grose designed and erected the headgear for Low's Shaft (Fig. 30) and installed the steam hoist and pump there. The engine house he had built was a small 'frame and galvanised building' containing just a boiler and engine, with storage place for fuel, and a small stack.[102] The steam pump was a 'duplex drive steam pump' and its cylinder size was about 4½ inches.[103] Sidney Grose, a mechanically experienced younger brother of Ambrose, came to take care of it.[104] William sometimes had to

30. Headgear at
Low's Shaft from S
(approx).
*Photographer not
known*

go and light the fire and get the steam up and keep the steam gauge at
65.[105] By using a theodolite and a piece of rag tied to the headframe, after
climbing the ladder (visible in Fig. 30), Ambrose made a small pond and
piped water to a tank in the engine room. Previously a barrel of water had
been used.[106]

The steam hoist was about ten times faster than the horse whim (it
took one minute rather than ten).[107] Although Low's Shaft is said to have
reached a depth of 316 ft (96.3m) in 1915,[108] it was only worked to the
24-fathom (144 ft) level in William Grose's day. After abandonment of
the horse whim, the ore was raised in a skip (essentially a wooden box on
guide rails) by a steam winding engine and tipped into a tram wagon at
the head of a self-acting gravity inclined tramway down towards the
stamps.

Simon Chivell was the engineman, and he slowed the rising skip
when it neared the top. Originally he had a white mark on a piece of rope
but later a proper dial was installed with a bicycle chain and strong
sprockets. It was marked with the 12-fathom level near the bottom and
the 24-fathom level near the top. There was also a bell connected to the
hoist – 3 rings were the signal for up, 2 for down and 1 for stop – there
was no other bell on the mine.[109]

Practically all the fuel used was peat (turf), cut by George Caunter. When the steam pump was working by itself, just peat was used for the boiler, but when the hoist was also in operation coal was added.[110] Some domestic coal was used by the family, and the blacksmith used high quality 'blacksmith's coal'.[111]

There were tanks at each level (12, 24 and 36 fathoms) in Low's Shaft as part of the pump mechanism (operated by flat rods) to raise water to the adit level, which was at 12 fathoms. Heavy chains connected each lift. William had been down the shaft several times and, one day when the miners had gone home, his father asked him to check whether or not the top tank was overflowing. If it was he was to 'hitch up the bottom one'.

'I went up there and had a candle and went down. Yes, it was overflowing. And I wanted to go down further and see what was happening to the other one...and I got down there to the bottom of it and there's a platform there...and the candle went out. I had matches but they wouldn't light in that flood of water going down there. I had no business down [there]... – I was only asked to see to the top one. I was exceeding my authority and ended up getting into trouble over it too. My father didn't like that kind of thing... So I thought, I've got to get out of here...Pitch dark...and so I felt the other ladder, pitch dark, a candle in my hand, matches in my pocket, felt that ladder. There was a manhole there, see, put your feet around. I thought I mustn't lose my head on this one. There's the other side of the ladder. A wooden ladder with iron staves. With two sides, and I hooked over my feet and I was standing in the middle. And I felt the bottom stave of that ladder. I'm on it, and I went up, you see, and the water streaming down over my head. Pitch dark, and I got to the other manhole – you've got to watch that your head doesn't knock that manhole...I kept in close...and I hadn't come to the staves by now. I'd normally [go] up one and feel another. Half a dozen first haul. And I believe there were probably twenty staves or more there...and so I felt the ladder, felt the ladder, up and up and up. Then this way and that way I felt the manhole, and on I went through that one, you see. And then the ladder ends there, so I run my hand up to the side of the ladder, see...that's that end...and I got on up out of the top. Then time to step off. I stepped off. And I got up on top. I got up on top, you know, and I was wet through. I expected that. Then I started for home...of course, the fact that I was wet wouldn't make any difference...they'd expect that...Father was come to see where I was, "Why've you been so long?". "It was dark down there, the water put my candle out, and I couldn't get my matches to light. I should have had a better match box". We had them there, you know. He didn't think I... I had no business going down that extra one. That's what the trouble was. Going beyond where I was told to go. He was suspicious, I could see that, and I was wet and tired and scared. I kept my head all the time. I didn't think I could do that. I was scared but I kept my head and I got out of there, came back...Mother was fussed up...I had a change of clothes. It was Saturday afternoon, you see. I had a change of clothes, and went on all right'.[112]

Lying on the ground in Fig. 30 are some large iron pipes which appear to be parts of Cornish pumps, powered by flat rods. These may be from some of the original pumps powered by the waterwheel below Low's Shaft, or they may be equipment about to be installed in Low's Shaft once the new flat rods were attached to the large wheel opposite Dry Lake.

Being adventurous, William once went up to Taylor's Shaft (SX 65087106) at Hensroost and noticed that some of the boards across the top were loose and thought to himself ,

> 'I'm going down there sometime. A little ways in there. The old ladders would be rotten...after all that time. Fool that I was. I went there once. It was a time my father went into Ashburton or something. I went down the first ladder, looked around. I had a candle. It was the same as Low's Shaft, nothing more to see there. I climbed up the ladder again and put the boards back and drove nails into the rock. Alone. Never said a word to mother about it. She didn't know it. Nobody knew it. This is the first [time] I've ever told it. I remember doing that. I've exceeded my business in a lot of things'.[113]

Underground trammers 'trammed the ore from the working face of the tunnel or "level" to the shaft & dumped [it] into the kibble to be hauled to the surface...The miners broke loose the ore & by the time the trammer loaded it & trammed it to the shaft & back there was another load ready. Note there was only one pair of miners in one tunnel working face.'[114] The miners worked in shifts 7am-2pm and 2pm-10pm. The 'day men' worked 7am-5pm with an hour for lunch.[115]
There were 8-12 miners and 2 trammers when William Grose was there.

> 'A miner was a higher grade employee than a trammer. A young man going underground first would start as a trammer & if he was good at it would be given a chance to go mining. Dicky Jones the old tin dresser was an ex-miner, his older son was a miner at Hexworthy. Jack, the younger, worked at the stamps & wanted to go underground (more money) & Father started him at it & I believe he later went on as a miner. There was already a trammer there, an elderly man named Abraham Heywood, who lived at Scoriton & walked to & fro from there everyday, very peculiar in speech and not considered "all there", very strong & a first class trammer'.[116]

Ladders were used to get underground. Miners were provided with candles and tools. At one time the workforce was cut down to between two and four miners.[117] Sometimes the air was bad, filled with dynamite smoke – you'd 'hardly be able to get a candle burning'.[118] There was no compressed air at Hexworthy until the modernisation of 1905-7.

William sometimes accompanied his father when he went underground to measure how far had been driven by miners under contract (so much a foot for the distance driven), holding a tape 'from an iron spike driven into the rock at the starting place'.[119] Some men worked by day but most by contract. Each miner made his own distinctive noise when hammering a drill – a combination of a grunt and a whistle, reflecting exhalation and inhalation of air, which helped keep the necessary rhythm of the work.[120] William was puzzled how miners communicated with each other when drilling as it was very noisy, but he observed how, when the miner holding the hand drill wished his partner to stop hammering (for example, so that the drilled hole could be cleaned out), he would stick his thumb out sideways while still holding the drill.[121] Only candles were used; there were no carbide lamps.[122]

The self-acting tramroad was 'constructed with a double track and a drum at the top with adequate brake for control'.[123] A wire rope was connected to both tram wagons. The full wagon going down pulled the empty one up, passing each other halfway. At the bottom of the incline, still some distance from the stamps, the tramroad became single track and wagons were pushed from there to the stamps. The full wagons were emptied into a hopper behind the stamps.[124]

In William Grose's day men are known to have travelled to Hexworthy Mine from Ashburton, Buckfastleigh, Clitters (Gunnislake), Lustleigh, Mary Tavy, Postbridge, Scoriton (Holne) and Whiteworks. Those from Scoriton and Buckfastleigh would come across the open moor, crossing the O Brook near Dry Lake, and carrying a horn lantern in winter.[125] The names of about 100 persons (miners and others) connected with the mine from the late nineteenth century have been identified so far.[126]

Only one photograph has come to light of men underground (Fig. 31),

31. Miners underground, probably in Low's Shaft, about 1910. *Photographer not known. Robin Hood collection*

32. Group of miners from Hexworthy Mine. *Photographer not known, Torquay Museum*

probably in Low's Shaft in about 1910. A ladder and a vertical pipe (perhaps for compressed air) can be seen in the background. None of the men has been identified with certainty.

A fine photograph (Fig. 32) of a group of miners, and probably dating to around 1910, was published in the *South Devon Journal* on 14 November 1956, claiming to be a group of men who worked at Hexworthy Mine. One miner, W. Bawden of Ashburton, said to be the son-in-law of Sally Satterley of Hexworthy, is identified as being fourth from right in the back row. Five other Ashburton men are named though not precisely identified – Milton, Wills, Durston, German and Bishop. These may well be Hexworthy miners, but the photograph was not taken on the mine itself as a lowland hedged background can be seen, so it may be that they were actually photographed at Owlacombe Mine near Ashburton or elsewhere. It was clearly taken at 'crib' time as some of the men are eating pasties.

Wives and relatives left at home were, not surprisingly, sometimes anxious about the wellbeing of their menfolk in such potentially dangerous work. Emily Coaker (born 1900) told me that when she was a girl of eleven or twelve she sometimes slept in her neighbour's house at The Mount, Holne to keep Mrs Warren company when her husband Ernest ('Baker') Warren was on nightshift at 'Hensroost'. He once got lost in 'a very deep fog'.[127] But maybe she needn't have worried too much as his nephew, Bill Warren of Scoriton, told me that his uncle and Fred Pearse once managed to fool the Captain that they were working but actually spent most of the night above ground in a shed.[128]

Harry Morris of Buckfastleigh and John (Jack) Warne (1875-1956) of Eastern Cottage, Postbridge both worked at Hexworthy. They are seen in a photograph of what must be the porch of the Mine House (Fig. 33). They also appear in the background on the right of a photograph, probably taken on the same warm summer's day, of the headgear at Low's Shaft (Fig. 30).

Jack Warne rose to the position of Captain. His recollections of time on the mine were printed with his obituary notice in the *Tavistock Times* on 12 October 1956:

'I started myself in the mine when I was 14 years of age. And I walked more than seven miles to work. Every Monday morning I walked to Hexworthy tin mine, beyond the Forest Inn. When I started to work in Hexworthy Mine there were many of us who used to walk miles to work Monday mornings. We would set off at five o'clock and, mark this, we would take our week's food with us. I used to take four to five pasties along with me. They would last me until Thursday. Then I always had some season pudding for Friday and, of course, on the Saturday we used to set off for home again. Certainly we were able to warm the grub up again. I have taken bacon and eggs and dried fish with me, the point being that I could not get food there. Where could we buy it? Don't think I had the hardest job of all the miners. Why a man called Inglewood used to walk in every Monday, and back home on Saturday, from South Zeal, and he brought his food with him too. At one time there were 25 to 30 men who came from Mary Tavy. But for them there was a man called Littlejohns who had a donkey and cart and he used to bring food out to the Mary Tavy men, all of whom at one time worked at the Friendship Mine, which had closed down. How did we manage about the cooking? Well, when I went first we had our own saucepans and frying pans, otherwise there would have been a terrible mix-up.

We used to start work at seven in the morning and leave off at two o'clock if we were on the morning shift and from two to ten if we were on the second shift. No matter how far we had to walk to work Monday mornings we had to be there on the dot of seven. I remember one time my boss said to me: 'John, you are a bit late this morning'. I said, 'Well,

33. Harry Morris and Jack Warne in porch of Mine House. *Photographer not known*

43

you know where I have come from this morning.' He said, 'Yes. I know. Don't come it too often. Time and tide wait for no man.' And I left home between four and five that morning! We had to get there. Times are different today. The youngsters of today won't believe me when I tell 'em.'

Jack (Jan) Warne was one of seven sons and two daughters of tin miner Solomon Warne and his wife Selina. At least six of these sons were miners. He himself married Amy, the daughter of Richard Jory of Vitifer Mine. His son Fernley told me in 1970 that his father wasn't paid for the last two years of his work at Hexworthy and recovered some of the money owed him by selling machinery from the mine.[129]

Jack Warne's brother Freddy (1879-1960), a very experienced miner, also worked at Hexworthy. In an article in a magazine he was recorded as saying that Hexworthy was a very dry mine, and

> 'the most beautiful little mine in Devon, and if anyone wanted to start mining tomorrow, that's where I'd tell them to start digging. I fixed the last blast down there on the day it closed, and we didn't gather that day's tin up so we could always say there's still tin on Dartmoor'.[130]

George Caunter was very adept at moving heavy objects, but sometimes men and horses were defeated. On one such occasion involving a very large piece of timber, George Smith, farmer of Hexworthy, said 'Ventor will do it!'. Ventor turned out to be a South Devon bull who was taken up to the mine, yoked up and put to the task, and the timber was successfully nudged into position.[131]

William Head was living at Coombe, Scoriton in 1901 when he was aged 44, and was 'a good man, a good miner'. At the Forest Inn he would 'get loaded the night before; the next day he was on the job'. He was said to have been cruel to his wife and she was exhumed.[132]

Jim and Fred Pearse were brothers from Scoriton who worked together – William Grose would 'see them come over the hill in the morning'. They would cross the O Brook near Drylake. One day, when returning from the mine, Jim Pearse met 'Squire Tanner' who asked, 'Well, Pearse, digging for gold?' to which he replied , 'Yes, sir, once a month', referring to when he was paid. Ernie Warren of Scoriton also worked with Fred Pearse. There was a shop at Scoriton called Crews, which sold supplies to the miners. In Jim Pearse's day you could buy a pint of beer, ½ an ounce of tobacco and a box of matches with 6d, and still have ½d in change.[133] Emily Coaker recalled that Jim Pearse was injured on a mine (quite possibly Hexworthy) and came to Chapel at Scoriton with his head bandaged.[134]

Sidney French of Middle Merripit, Postbridge (1889-1976) worked there for six to eight months before transferring to Golden Dagger Mine – 'go down Mondays and come back Saturdays, or Fridays', 'bagged up' with pasties and 'Season Pudding' (potato, onion and meat in pastry, boiled in a cloth). They would hand this to a man who would heat it up in a saucepan in readiness for when they came up from underground.[135]

One of the first stories I heard relates to a miner whose pasties were not in best condition by the end of the week, as one can imagine in hot summer weather. When other miners remonstrated with him at the prospect of eating a pasty with maggots in it, the old miner's practical approach to the situation was to say, 'If you buggers are going to eat my pasty, I'm going to eat you!'.[136]

Salted dried cod known as 'Toregg' (= toerag) was a favourite staple of John Warne and others.[137] Annie Sleep recalled that the miners used to soak it in the leat and that cats soon 'got wise to that'.[138]

Wages were paid every two weeks –

> 'pay day [was] on the Saturday of the second week. At the end of the first week father made out a "Cost Sheet" of all the hours each man worked & their wages, other expenses for the preceding two weeks, added the total & sent it to Mr Bayldon at Dawlish, & he sent by return a cheque for the total as sent to him. The following Friday John Cleave of the Forest Inn took him to Ashburton & he cashed the check at the Capital & Counties bank there, brought it home & the pay day was next day, Saturday at midday. Sometimes he went around by Buckfastleigh, to Willcocks & Son about castings and machine work for the mine. Occasionally I went with him & sometimes Mother went for shopping'.[139]

John (Jan) Cleave charged six shillings for the trip.[140]

William Grose commented that 'Half of them couldn't read or write' but they

> 'made more money mining and... they'd got a fatal attraction for it...they seemed to just love it'.[141] 'The miners seemed to amuse themselves...they would go down to the Forest Inn & drink beer when off shift, usually Monday nights after their Saturday & Sunday home. They played cards. They seemed to be happy & contented...Jack Jones trapped rabbits [though] it was not allowed by the moor authorities...everyone was in good health. I don't remem-

34. The Forest Inn, Hexworthy 1892. *Photographer not known. Devon Library Services E/C/7542*

ber a Doctor ever being required – this applied to our family as well. It was a healthy place...' [142]

The Forest Inn (Fig. 34) was 'an old dilapidated thatch covered place', which was rebuilt while the Groses were there.[143] It had 'an open chimney peat fire, a flintlock gun over the shelf over the open chimney, stone floor. Dartmoor farmers drinking beer at a table. There was no bar.'[144]

The Grose family left Hexworthy late in 1903,[145] and a major and expensive programme of further modernisation under new lessees, soon followed. This marked the last phase of working of the mine which lasted until about the end of the First World War. Dartmoor Minerals Ltd was registered on 21 July 1905 with its directors being Lord Armstrong of Cragside, Northumberland, Sir Augustus C. F. Fitzgeorge of 6 Queen St, Mayfair, London and H. Maconochie of Heath Brow Cottage, Hampstead.[146] The company had 15,000 shares of £1 each.[147] It held a lease of 'Henroost Mine', and also leases of Great Whiteworks Mines, Golden Dagger Mine and East Birch Tor Bounds, comprising together in total 'an area of over six square miles'. The report noted that

> 'The Henroost Mine was unwatered last year [1906] and is kept dry by a two-lift Cornish pump. An incline shaft has been sunk on the lode, 12ft. by 6ft., to a depth of 35½ fathoms from surface, and three levels have been put out at 11½ fathoms (or adit level), 24 and 35 fathoms and these drives north and south have proved the lode laterally for 1,546 feet. The shaft is now being re-timbered, and a double skipway put in with ore bins at collar and each level.'[148]

A commissioned report by Jervis Veale, dating to approximately 1909/10, while recognising 'the extraordinary general productiveness of the lode', was highly critical of management of the mine and the expenditure on surface equipment rather than development of underground workings. In his opinion it was 'absolutely unwarranted and deserves the strongest condemnation and criticism at the hands of any engineer'. He pointed out that the new mill was designed for dealing with 'not less than 1,000 tons per month, equal to 13,000 tons per annum, against actually crushed during 12 months, from Dec.19th 1907 to Dec. 16th 1908 2,137 tons or only one sixth of its full capacity. Moreover only half the mill had worked for only 348 hours per month when it had the capacity in full work, to employ 10 heads of stamps for 1,248 hours. He

35. View of Low's Shaft and dressing floors from N, about 1915.
Miss May

analysed one month of production and cost and calculated that profit was
just 6s 8d! He concluded that

> 'It will be difficult to find a more glaring instance of mismanagement and
> administration...It has rarely been my lot to report on a more promising
> undertaking...and it has rarely been my lot to see one so badly worked and
> managed'.[149]

In 1907 the New Mill (Fig. 35) was described as follows: 'here is erected
a 10-stamp of 1,062lbs stamps, with ore bins of Fraser and Chalmers
latest type. Room for an additional 10 heads is allowed for. There is also
a 15in. by 9in. Blake Rock-breaker with Challenge Ore feeders, together
with Wilfley Tables and one Wilfley Slime Table. An elevated tramway
conveys the ore from the shaft to this building.' The new Engine House
or Power House contained 'motor for driving mill, crusher and
concentrating plant, and also the dynamo, switchboards etc'. The Electric
Hoist was of 'the Lidgerwood Double Friction Drum type, with lever
brakes and 500 volt motor complete.'[150] Frank Warne (born 1901)
remembered that the Engine House also contained an air compressor and
electrically operated pumps.[151] Fig. 36 shows the New Engine House
behind the headframe of Low's Shaft. The rails in the foreground led to

three distinct waste tips. The line of pumping rods from the wheel opposite Dry Lake can be seen approaching from the right.

The Turbine or Generator House (Figs 37-8) was located at Saddle Bridge at SX 66427192, and described as 'a steel structure, 44ft. by 24ft. and has space for additional plant if extra power is required at any time. The plant consists of a 6ft. Pelton Wheel, with electric governor to drive continuous current generator of 110 k.w. With the available water power it is estimated to develop 147 h.p'. It was supplied by the Wheal Emma Leat: 'The excavations, 3¼ miles in length for this leat, which averages 4ft. deep, are now completed, and the water is conveyed to the Pelton Wheel by a 16in. rolled steel pipe line, the fall at the intake of leat to nozzle at wheel being 183 feet.'[152] Bunny Spiller recalled that a walking stick would bounce off the powerful jet of water striking the cups of the Pelton Wheel.[153]

Horses and carts were hired from local farmers for various requirements. Silas Sleep and Matthew White of Postbridge used to drag timber out of Brimpts and take it to the mine for 5 shillings or 7s 6d for the day. They also took tin to Princetown station, as did a man called Stabb.[154] 'People used to look in the cart and laugh because they'd see the poor horses tugging up the hill...and see these little bags in the bottom of the cart' – about half a ton of tin.[155] Frank Warne (born 1901) said the bags were made of sailcloth and that it would take three or four men to lift one into a cart, and that only two bags would be put in a cartload.[156] George Michelmore of Poundsgate delivered telegrams and supplies by horse and cart during the First World War.[157] Bill Lance of Hexworthy also hired out his horse and cart for the mine.[158]

The Census for 1911 records unmarried 25-year-old Leonard Harvey living at the mine, when he was described as 'Joint Manager of Tin Mine'. He was born in Penzance. Also on the mine, probably in the Mine House, was the Perryman family. John Perryman, aged thirty, was described as 'Stationary Engineman'. He was born in Teignmouth. His wife Caroline, also aged thirty, lived with him and their four children – John (8), Fredrick (4), Ada (3) and Helen (1 month).

An account published in 1912 said that in the New Mill

> 'material from the stamps passes successively to 3 classifiers, whence it passes to the Wilfley tables and a revolving slime table. The final operations consists of buddling the concentrates, passing them over a square sloping frame and treating them in kieves. The black tin recently sold from the mine is so pure that it fetches the highest price in the market.'[159]

In 1915-16 the mine produced 13½ tons of black tin. The last underground work was carried out by a team headed by an Australian miner in the summer of 1919. A storm in 1920 caused serious flooding and demolished the launder leading to the pumping wheel. This caused the head of Low's Shaft to collapse and thus the mine was flooded. Proposals were made in 1925 to re-open the mine but nothing was done.[160]

38. Turbine House from E on postcard titled 'Dartmoor Hills' about 1915. *Photographer not known*

39. Abandoned
waterwheel
opposite Dry Lake
from NE (approx),
with Mrs Spiller,
August 1917.
M. Spiller

40. Abandoned
waterwheel
opposite Dry Lake
from NW (approx),
August 1917.
M. Spiller

HEXWORTHY MINE – BACK TO THE LAND

By the end of the First World War it seems that the mine infrastructure was largely abandoned. Fortunately a few surviving photographs illustrate aspects of this. Several (Figs 39-42) show the large waterwheel opposite Dry Lake, between August 1917 and about 1920. The wheel was dismantled in 1935.[161] Of special interest is an image (Fig. 43) of Geraldine May and a friend sitting in a tram wagon on rails which led from the adit at Hooten Wheals i.e. the 12-fathom level at Low's Shaft. This tramway did not exist in William Grose's day as the adit was

41. Abandoned waterwheel opposite Dry Lake from W (approx) about 1918. *Photographer not known, ex Irene Mary Wellington*

42. Abandoned
waterwheel
opposite Dry Lake
from W (approx)
about 1920, with
children.
*Photographer not
known, ex Marion
Howard*

43. Geraldine May
and friend in
abandoned tram by
adit at Hooten
Wheals, 1919.
*Photographer not
known, ex Marion
Howard*

44. New Mill and
dressing floors
apparently
abandoned, about
1920. *Photographer
not known, ex M.
Perriam*

then merely for drainage, and so must have been installed about 1905-7.
It led directly to the New Mill dressing floors, which are shown in Fig.
44, apparently then in an abandoned state. The vertical lifters of
Californian stamps can just be seen on the extreme left.

The turbine house by Saddle Bridge is captured in the background of
this photograph from the mid-1920s (Fig. 45). The car was registered in
Buckinghamshire.

The Engine House although ruined (Fig. 46) still contained remnants
of *in situ* machinery which were photographed by Peter Richardson in the

45. Turbine House by Saddle Bridge about 1925. *Photographer not known, ex Wendy Lamble*

1930s (Figs 47-8). In the 1960s and 1970s the present author recorded flanged wheels on which pumping flatrods were supported, and also the remains of an iron kibble i.e. a bucket for hauling ore (Figs 49-50).

Local people remembered seeing the abandoned site with papers and furniture still left in the buildings. Rabbits were flushed from underneath the suspended floor of the Iron House with ferrets by the Chaffe family[162] and by Kenneth Williams (born c.1912) by jumping up and down on the floor, having spread nets around the building.[163] George Robertson Owen (born 1919) remembered visiting the site in the late 1920s and noting

46. View to Engine House at Low's Shaft and New Mill from N (approx) in 1941. *S. Taylor*

47. View from Low's Shaft looking E (approx), 14 August 1938. *P. H. G. Richardson*

48. Remains of winding gear in Engine House by Low's Shaft, 22 August 1934. *P. H. G. Richardson*

49. Flanged wheels of two different designs, for flat rods (for pumping), 11 September 1968 (18¾ in x 2½ in) and 13 February 1977 (Scale: 15cm).
T. Greeves

that everything seemed to have been left in a hurry. There was 'dirty washing', 'dirty crockery' and 'elementary furniture' left in the mine accommodation and, in a shed, circular pits still full of material waiting to be dug out.[164]

Much of the complex was badly damaged, with the Mine House, Dry, Blacksmith's Shop and Engine House all being razed, and the New Mill used as target practice by American troops training for D-Day in 1944.

In October 1980 Dartmoor National Park Authority shored up the wheelpit opposite Dry Lake with massive timbers.

50. Remains of iron kibble, 1968.
T. Greeves

VITIFER MINE

On moorland Dartmoor, at a height of between 1,200-1,400ft (365-425m) OD, the upper portion of the Redwater valley which flows into the Webburn, and ultimately the River Dart, contains an extraordinary tinworking landscape covering more than two square kilometres (Fig. 51). Essentially it is an abandoned industrial landscape of the medieval period, with huge opencast gullies, where tinners laboriously hacked out rich tin lodes between about AD 1200 and 1600, but perhaps even from prehistoric times. It does not take an explorer long to realise that there are later features here too – ruins of buildings and wheelpits etc – some of which were still in use in the first half of the twentieth century.

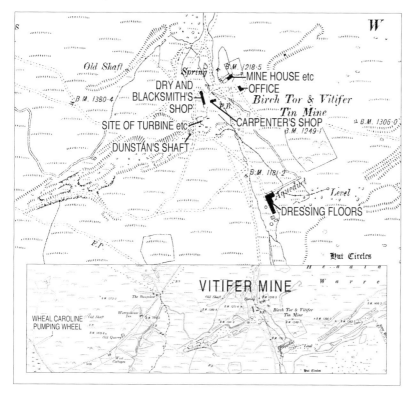

51. Map of Vitifer Mine and Wheal Caroline pumping wheel, based on OS 2nd edn 6-inch, 1906, Sheet 99NE (not to scale)

52. Old tin
workings, Old
Vitifer Lode, and
site of Dunstan's
Shaft. *Chapman &
Son 11956*

We have no certain surviving documentation for tinworking here
before 1750[165] which marks the approximate start of a resurgence of
mining, with deep shafts. Vitifer (usually pronounced 'Vytifer' by
Dartmoor people) is the name most commonly applied, though strictly
speaking Birch Tor & Vitifer is more correct as these two mines were often
worked together.

Throughout much of the nineteenth century the mine was worked on
a large scale, but conditions and its reputation were not always good – in
1835 'wretched' accommodation caused beds to be occupied continuously
throughout the different shifts over a 24-hour period, and lawlessness in
the area as a whole caused the vicar of Widecombe to refer to Dartmoor in
1837 as a 'Botany Bay for Miners'. A description of the mine in the mid-
1830s claimed that bad air underground, through lack of ventilation,
'killed scores of miners', and at much the same time, on the unroofed
dressing floors on the surface, with no protection from the elements,
'women are wrapped up against the wind and the rain and the children do
cry of the cold' .[166]

The Old Vitifer Lode, seen in Fig. 52, was on the west side of the valley and is representative of many colossal openwork gullies in the complex. Moses Bawden (1834-1916), one of the most highly respected mine managers in Devon and Cornwall in the late nineteenth century, who was involved with the mine from 1864-1902, commented, 'Tens of millions of tons of stuff must have been taken out of them to get down to water level. I know of no such evidence of ancient mining in any part of Devon and Cornwall as is seen here'. He had been told that, in the first half of the nineteenth century, John Paull had made £60,000-£80,000 profit from working the Birch Tor Lode to a depth of 70 fathoms (420ft/130m), partly financed by Richard and Stephen Davey of Cornwall.[167] A figure in the foreground gives scale. Behind him can be seen the top of the inverted cone of Dunstan's Shaft (see Fig. 2). More ancient workings are seen in Fig. 53, with a view to the iconic Warren House Inn.

53. Old tin workings and Warren House Inn. *Chapman & Son 11960*

54. General view of Vitifer Mine buildings with Birch Tor, from SW (approx). *Chapman & Son 11954*

55. Miners' Bunk House and Mine Captain's House, Vitifer Mine, about 1910. *Chapman & Son 11954, detail*

The principal buildings at Vitifer Mine in about 1900 are shown in Figs 54 and 55, with Birch Tor behind. Most are now reduced to meagre foundations. The lefthand building was a Carpenter's Shop. All the other buildings are on the east side of the stream. The large two-storey building is the Miners' House, Bunk House or 'Crib' House where men lodged for the week who travelled from outlying villages and towns. A short flight of steps led up to a door in its west-facing gable end. The ground floor was essentially one large room with a long table and 'a great big stove' for heating up the miners' food. The widow of William Warne (born 1897), the son of Capt. William Warne, recalled that it was the job of younger men and boys, such as her husband, to heat up the pasties and make the tea.[168]

There was also space for drying clothes. Upstairs there was a narrow central passage and, on either side, it was 'parted up' with matchboard to create little cubicles just big enough for a bed.[169] Each cubicle had an oil lamp. Lewis Evely (1886-1971) cycled to the mine from Whiddon Down and from Shilstone Farm, Throwleigh, sometimes leaving two hours early 'to trim the lamps'.[170] Parties or concerts were held there once or twice a year.[171] Mr & Mrs Slade acted as housekeepers/caretakers and lived downstairs.[172] Gertrude Chudley (born 1892) of Gobbett, as a teenager in about 1907/8, looked after one of their children (Fig. 56), and also Arthur Willcocks, a Down's Syndrome child of H. M. D. Willcocks who was 'Chief Agent' at Birch Tor & Vitifer 1904-1913.[173] The Miners' House was last used in the late 1920s when refurbished by Donald

56. Gertrude Chudley with a Slade child at Vitifer c.1907. *Photographer not known, ex Mrs Prew*

Smith for his Golden Dagger workforce from Plymouth.[174] He recalled that there was one large room (for meals and use as a common room) on the ground floor, and two smaller rooms, one of which was used as a kitchen, and the other 'where an old chap from Plymouth and his wife slept'. Water came from a spring behind the building.[175]

Adjoining the Bunk House is a substantial thatched stone cottage, the oldest building in the complex and perhaps dating to the eighteenth century. This was the Mine Captain's House. It had four upstairs bedrooms and three rooms downstairs — kitchen, sitting room and scullery/pantry/larder. Anna Jory, wife of Captain Richard Jory, told her granddaughter Elsie Coaker that at the time of the Great Blizzard of March 1891 it was possible to walk out of the bedroom windows onto the snow. The Jorys always kept a bag of flour and a sack of potatoes handy for emergencies, and would salt down a pig for the winter.[176]

Attached to the thatched building is another house of more recent (perhaps late nineteenth-century) construction, and was occupied by other miners and their families.

Garden enclosures adjoined the north side of these buildings. John Hannaford of Headland Warren used to till these and potatoes, cabbages and gooseberries were among produce grown.[177]

The detached west-facing building with its prominent porch was the Mine Office where accounts would be kept and men paid their wages (Fig. 57). It has substantial chimney stacks at the rear and appears to be stone-built and perhaps of mid-nineteenth century date. It is probably where the mine bell was hung, marking the change of shifts.[178] Captain John James Coaker and his family lived here for several years from 1896 before moving to Postbridge and then Dinah's House, Golden Dagger. Their daughter Elsie was born in an upstairs room in 1896. As a young girl she had to collect milk from Headland Warren Farm where Mrs Hannaford sometimes gave her bread and cream to eat. Bakers delivered to the mine from Chagford, Poundsgate and Widecombe. One used to have mishaps with 4lb loaves not infrequently tipping out of his cart, after spending time in the Warren House Inn.[179]

A single-storey bungalow, with additional accommodation at the rear, housed miners and their families. It is of late nineteenth-century or early twentieth-century date. Uphill behind it, the roof of a small building is visible in a gully – this was known as Kits House Gully[180] but the function of the building is unknown.

A grander bungalow, partly of brick, with a glass and wood verandah (Fig. 58) was sited on a terrace a short distance upslope towards Headland Warren. Most of the mine complex was visible from it. It was built for the mine manager, the 'boss of all', William Albert Padfield of Exeter, who was granted a 31-year lease of Birch Tor & Vitifer from Michaelmas 1903 by the Duchy of Cornwall.[181] It was burnt down, probably not long before the First World War.

58. Manager's
bungalow. *Chapman
& Son 11955 detail*

59. Four men
working
underground at
Vitifer. *Chapman &
Son 11943*

The underground workings of Vitifer in the early twentieth century were on the east side of the valley running underneath great gullies extending towards Headland Warren. Fig. 59 shows two pairs of men working underground, at two levels, hammering and drilling holes by hand into hard rock for explosive charges. Three of the men have taken off their hard hats exposing the flannel skull-caps underneath. The man top

60. Memorial to
John Webb in
Postbridge church.
T. Greeves

60. Memorial to John Webb in Postbridge church. *T. Greeves*

right has a candle stuck to his hat, and the two patches of brightness to the left of the picture are also likely to be candles, fixed to the rock with lumps of clay. The cheerful appearance of the men belies conditions which were described variously as 'very wet', 'rugged' and 'streaming down' with water, and with air quality bad enough in places to make candles go out.[182]

The top two men are unidentified, but the lower two are Frederick (Freddy) Warne (1879-1960) on the left, and John (Jack) Webb (1877-1916) on the right. Freddy, who was also known as 'Nicky Toody',[183] was from a mining family and was one of seven brothers, at least five of whom were tin miners. He was known to be immensely strong. He survived fighting in France in 1918 and worked at Golden Dagger in the 1920s (see below). John Webb (1877-1916) was not so lucky, being killed in France on 21 August 1916, aged thirty-nine, when serving with an infantry battalion of the 2nd Devons.[184] A memorial plaque for him is in Postbridge church (Fig. 60). He was remembered as having 'a lovely tenor voice', and for singing carols underground at Christmas time.[185] His daughter recalled[186] that one of his favourite songs was 'Till the Sands of the Desert Grow Cold' by Ball and Graff, which had been published in 1911. Although born in Postbridge, John Webb worked for a time in Bristol as a Post Office engineer but returned to Dartmoor in about 1905 on account of his father's ill-health. He is said to have worked at Whiteworks Mine and to have lived in New London, Princetown as well as Powder Mills.[187] When working at Vitifer, he walked from Princetown and stayed at Stannon Lodge, Postbridge with 'old Tom Webb' and walked daily to and from the mines.[188]

61. Three men
underground at
Vitifer. *Chapman &
Son 11944*

VITIFER + BIRCH TOR TIN MINE. POST BRIDGE 11944

Fig. 61 is another underground scene, showing three men in relatively cramped conditions underground at Vitifer Mine, on two levels, with the lower man standing on a wooden platform known as a sollar or stull. The top two men are not certainly identified but the lower figure is Sidney French (1889-1976) who also worked underground at Golden Dagger and Hexworthy. At Vitifer there were three 8-hour shifts in 24 hours: forenoon (7am-3pm), afternoon (3pm-11pm) and night (11pm-7am). Sidney vividly recalled conditions:

> 'Of course in some places, 'twould be very bad working, you know. You'd [be] in an end, you'd blast two or three or three or four holes, and you'd have the dynamite smoke. Well, they'd blast, say, half past two, and you'd go in three o'clock. Well the place 'twould be all full of smoke sometimes, you see. That was bad. But of course, sometimes where you was up, stoping up, twould be more air like – the smoke would go, you see. But in an end it would be bad sometimes, yes'.[189]

Sidney French was from a farming family living at Middle Merripit, Postbridge and had eight brothers, two of whom were also miners. He began work at Vitifer on 3 February 1903 earning 1s 9d per day as a buddle boy. He was about seventeen when he first went underground and eventually earned 24 shillings per week, which was considered good pay. He was paid fortnightly and had to put sixpence aside for the doctor in case of illness or injury.[190]

Sidney recalled that his breakfast mostly consisted of 'a cup of tea and a piece of bread and cream'. Sometimes he had 'kittle broth', which was bread in a basin with hot water or tea poured over it and with a lump of butter added. Occasionally he would have a piece of cake. His nephew Claude Warne remembered him setting off on the 2-mile walk to the mines with his (Sidney's) older brother Dick French (who was killed in the First World War) and Silas Sleep, and returning in a dirty state and washing in a stream with a bucket which would turn to mud.[191]

In the summer, Sidney was expected to help with the hay harvest on local farms. One year, at Runnage Farm, after an 8-hour forenoon shift at the mine,

> 'Us went back every...afternoon of the week. Cor, Saturday I was...Saving hay for ten, half past ten. Then you'd go in, have supper and then you had to walk home from Runnage to Merripit then out again half past five, quarter to six. Oh, I was runned up...!'.[192]

He survived the First World War, in India and Mesopotamia and eventually took on his father's farm.

His employment was due to a major revival of the mine, reported by the *West Briton* newspaper on 13 August 1903:

> 'After being closed for about 30 years. This mine has been re-started during the past few days, and is said to offer promises of good returns to the promoters of the venture. Capt. Webb, the manager of the new undertaking, was himself employed on the mine in his younger days, and has always felt the utmost confidence in making it a paying concern with the aid of up-to-date machinery. Assisted by the enterprise of Mr. W. R. Phelips, of Montacute, Somerset, and Mr. W. A. Padfield, of Exeter, he started twelve

months ago to clean up the property, and got it into proper working order. A new water wheel driving sixteen heads of stamps has been erected, and the entire motive power is supplied by water. In the vicinity are burrows of thousands of tons of stuff raised in the old days, and this is now being treated, with, we understand, good result. It is stated that the mine contains an unlimited supply of tin of excellent quality, and a lode is at present being driven on at a very slight depth. About 20 men are employed on the venture. On Wednesday of last week the *employés* were invited to meet the promoters at a dinner held on the mine. Mr. W. R. Phelips presided, and was supported by Messrs. W. A. Padfield, G. J. Richards (inspector of mines and quarries for the Duchy of Cornwall), H. M. Wilcocks, Capt. Webb, and others.

After the loyal toasts had been submitted, Mr Richards proposed "Success to Mining," to which the chairman, Mr. W. A. Padfield, responded.

In submitting the toast of "Capt. Webb and the Workmen," Mr. Padfield said that he was sure that Capt. Webb would leave no stone unturned to make the mine successful. A fortune had been made out of the mine in years past with tin at £30 per ton, and there was no reason why another fortune should not be made out of it with tin at double the price.

Responding to the toast, Capt. Webb remarked that the property had been locked up for thirty years and for half that period he had been endeavouring to secure the means to re-start it. He believed it was a genuine property, and one which would pay well for developing. There were tens of thousands of tons of stuff on the surface which were waiting to be dealt with, and, with modern dressing machinery, he did not think it would be long before they were able to show a good return for the working'.[193]

The mention of the mine having been 'closed' and 'locked up' for thirty years is something of an exaggeration, as clearly the buildings were occupied and a certain level of work was carried on during this period.

In early September 1904 the *West Briton* reported that a 'Wetherill magnetic separator plant is to be erected by the Vitifer Mine', which would make it only the fourth throughout Devon and Cornwall.[194]

A newspaper dated 17 August 1907 reported,

'All the machinery is worked by electricity, which is laid throughout the mine...The Secretary of the Company is Mr H. M. D. Wilcocks, who also acts as manager of the mine, which gives employment to about 40 men, Mr. W. J. Bennetts being the Captain.

At present the workings are in a horizontal line, the quartz being blasted and dug out of the side of a Tor, but it is proposed to shortly begin digging in a vertical direction. The quartz is taken in trolleys to the sixteen stamps which are working continuously, and there it is ground to powder, which consists of tin, iron, and sand...the powder is distributed over three buss tables consecutively and washed in such a manner that the best tin goes into one tank, the iron into another, and the sand into a third. It is then dried on large ovens and put through a magnetic separator, and this draws every particle of iron from the tin, which has realised the record price of £132 17s 6d per ton... The output of the mine at present is about two tons of black tin per month, and it is sent to Princetown by road, and then trained to Camborne or Redruth, where it is smelted...

Yesterday [Friday 16 August] the directors of the Company entertained their employes [sic] and a few visitors, the company numbering about fifty, which was served in excellent style in the "long room". Mr. R.P. Phelips presided, and he was supported by the Rev. Lester Cole (Postbridge), Messrs. W. A. Padfield, E. Stamp, M. Bawden (Tavistock), H. Higgs (Basingstoke), H. M. D. Wilcocks (manager), W. C. C. Rafarel, H. C. Wilcocks and W. J. Bennetts (captain of the mine)...

An enjoyable entertainment was afterwards provided, Mr Harry Rice, the well-known society entertainer, of Exeter, giving an excellent ventriloquial and conjuring performance, which was much appreciated, as were also selections on the gramophone by Messrs Westcott and Bowhay.'[195]

This was more or less the end of the period in which John Thomas of Camborne (1861-c.1946) found work on the mine for a few years, through his father's acquaintance with Capt. Bennetts. Although a farmer's son, he had already had experience working in mines in Montana, USA and in South Africa. His son, Garfield Thomas (born 1895) recalled how it happened:

'At Redruth Fair one Whit Saturday, my father met Capt. Bennetts who was home for a few days holiday from Birch Tor Mine...Of course they had a long talk about the mine and Capt. Bennetts said he wanted someone like my father to straighten things up and get going, and he persuaded my father to go back with him for a week or two. This he did and stayed 3 years. During that time my father lived with Capt. Bennetts in a Cottage on the mine and my mother and me spent several Holidays up there... We stayed several times with Miss Leaman's family at Dury Farm...I remember there was a sort of wood and galvanised Bunk House on the end of the Cottage where several of the mine workers ate and slept. There were 3 or 4 miners who used to come up from Gunnislake. They would come up Monday mornings by pony and trap and go home for weekends. There was one named Kemp I think who gave my father a lot of trouble. There was a wood Bungalow on the mine where Mr & Mrs Wilcocks and son Carberry lived. Mr Wilcocks was the Managing Director of the mine, and the Chairman Director was a Mr. Padfield who used to come out from Exeter about once a month, and he had a Bungalow opposite the Warren House Inn...At that time the tin used to be sold at Tabbs Hotel, Redruth, in what was known as the Tin Ticketing, and the Birch Tor tin always fetched the top price. I remember my father very pleased once when a

Birch Tor sample made £130 per ton. When my father finished at Birch Tor he started at South Crofty as a Timberman, when they started to sink New Cooks Shaft. In fact, he put the first set of timber in New Cooks Shaft. He was at South Crofty 27 years.'[196] He gained a colourful reputation at South Crofty where he was known as 'Johnny Boo', and was considered a stern taskmaster.[197]

62. Vitifer dressing floors and waterwheel from SE about 1910. *Photographer not known*

Fig. 62 shows the sheds that contained the Vitifer dressing floors at SX 68328071. The top of the large stamps waterwheel (40ft x 5ft/12 x 1.5m) can be seen above the top of the sheds. The large timber launder leading to it is clearly visible. The pale heap below and parallel with the launder is the line of the tramway that led from the adit and underground workings further east. The chimney was linked to equipment for drying the ore. A small waterwheel beside the chimney probably operated mechanical 'packing' of kieves (see Fig. 65). Although the site may well have been used for processing ore from at least the mid-nineteenth century (see Fig. 2), in this form the complex is likely to date to 1902/1903 as Sidney French recalls that when he began work in February 1903 a new wheelpit was being made and the wheel installed.[198] In the background, through the launder, some of the mine buildings can be seen, including the Dry (with chimney, on left), the Carpenter's Shop, and the Bunk House.

John Dawe of Higher Lydgate, Postbridge, was in charge of the stamps – Sidney French recalled that he was an old man at the time.[199] According to Frank Warne (born 1901) who worked here from 1914, once crushed by the stamps, the tin ore was taken to kieves and then jigging 'buss tables' before being transferred by launder to three round buddles outside the sheds, to undergo further separation of waste and initial

63. Round buddle and boys outside Vitifer dressing floors about 1910. *Chapman & Son 11950, ex Neil Parkhouse*

concentration.[200] Fig. 63 shows these buddles with boys at work, with a view up the valley to the mine buildings. The buddle has been completely dug out. Fig. 64 shows the same area, with an adult tin dresser at work. Timberwork and gearing are visible. What look like heaps of sand are in fact piles of tin ore waiting to be washed through the buddle. A glistening

64. Tin dresser and round buddle outside Vitifer dressing floors, about 1905. *Photographer not known*

VITIFER i BIRCH TOR TIN MINE   POST BRIDGE 11949

65. Interior of
Vitifer dressing
floors about 1910.
*Chapman & Son
11949*

buddle can be seen behind the unidentified man. A distinctive
wheelbarrow is in the foreground, and Birch Tor can just be seen on the
top left of the image. For a more detailed description of the buddling
process see Fig. 103 and pp 100-101.

Fig. 65 is a wonderfully informative image of the interior of the
dressing floor sheds. When I first saw it, it was propped on the mantelpiece
of Sidney French's home in Highweek. He handed it to me and, pointing
to the foreground figure, asked, 'Who's this yer boy then?' It was him. He
is in the process of stirring or digging out a large wooden tub known as a
kieve or chimming kieve, and the man behind him, Tom Webb (1865-
1957), has his hand resting on another.[201] Donald Smith's described the
kieving process, which was the stage following the outside round buddles,
based on his experience at Golden Dagger Mine in the late 1920s:

> 'A kieve was half-filled with water and the water stirred by a rotary action with
> a special shovel in the hands of one man, while the heads (concentrates) were
> introduced a little at a time by another worker, until anything up to 3cwt was
> in suspension in the water. This is very hard work when the water becomes like
> thin mud. When the tin dresser judges the time is right, the stirring stops and
> the side of the kieve is tapped to help the particles to settle in the kieve and pack
> down hard. The heavier tin will settle first and when the water is poured out
> the kieve, now on its side, would be in a good position for the tin dresser to
> scrape the top surface away for 'tailings' and the next inch or two for 'middles',
> and the bottom section as 'heads' which is judged for quality by vanning a little
> sample and noting the width of the tin band. Chimming kieves varied slightly
> in size, the smaller being used for the final chimming before bagging.'[202]

Several piles of crushed tin ore 'concentrate' are visible. The one nearest the foreground has a small chimming kieve in front of it, with a vanning shovel laid across it.

Of special interest is evidence of mechanical 'packing' of the kieve. Usually an iron bar ('bar ire') was used manually for this (see Fig. 132) but a device worked by a waterwheel was installed at Vitifer, involving woodwork seen behind the kieves and ironwork and gearing made by blacksmith Will Lentern.[203] A kieve was slightly tilted (one can just be made out behind Tom Webb) and then hit by an 'arm' with tappets.

The ore was then dried on 'a huge fire with an iron top' and resembled 'black gunpowder',[204] before being put through a magnetic separator. From there it went to a square buddle.

In the centre of the picture is a white-bearded man holding a long-handled shovel. This is Capt. Richard Jory (Captain Dick) (c.1847-1915), a Cornishman who managed Vitifer and Golden Dagger mines under Moses Bawden in the late nineteenth century. Beside him is a square buddle, in the form of a rectangular pit set into the floor, into which tin concentrate with water was carefully fed from a sloping surface (directly behind Richard Jory). The tin settled out in three grades – heads, middles and tails. This was an ancient technique and would not have been unfamiliar to medieval tinners.

One of the last processes remembered by Frank Warne was to put the concentrate through a 'tye...like a long launder' where it was worked up with a square shovel. Some of the tin would be 'like little peas'. The final tin concentrate was taken to the padlocked Tin Chest. The tin dresser would even take his boots off to wash off any valuable tin. Frank Warne commented 'it was rather interesting work'. [205]

66. Vitifer waterwheel, dressing floors and settling pits about 1905. *Photographer not known, ex David Edgcombe*

67. Vitifer miners.
Chapman & Son
11947

Two different types of wheelbarrow are visible in the background. More remarkable are the three electric lightbulbs, complete with lampshades. These were powered by an innovative water turbine, a short distance further up the valley by Dunstan's Shaft. Frank Warne, who started work in 1914, having reached the seventh standard at school, recalled using discarded bulbs as primitive barometers –

> '...if we had one fused, we used to knock the nib off, full 'im with water and 'ang 'im up...if it was going to be wet he'd start to drip. If it was going to dry weather with the dry air he'd keep the water in.'[206]

Fig. 66 shows the Vitifer waterwheel, stamps and sheds in a view looking down the valley towards Golden Dagger, probably in about 1906. Of interest are the pale settling pits to hold waste material (like a china clay mica dam). These may be the pits recommended in May 1906 by Windeatt & Windeatt, solicitors of Totnes, to be dug in order to prevent pollution to fisheries and other interests on the R. Dart. Two pits each 90ft x 30ft x 8-9ft deep were proposed, as were two smaller pits 30ft x 8ft x 4ft depth.[207]

The settling pits can traced on the ground today, but the site of the dressing floors has been destroyed, through the detonation of unexploded bombs brought out from Plymouth in the Second World War.[208] Just visible in the image is the roof of the Golden Dagger Dry and also the original Golden Dagger stamps wheel.

Eight miners are shown in characteristic clothing in Fig. 67, standing outside a building which may be the Dry, which was part of the complex on the west side of the valley at Vitifer. Of special interest is the fact that three brothers are in the picture – Henry (Harry 'Silvertop') Warne (1877-1941) on the extreme left, Frederick (Freddy 'Nicky Toody') Warne (1879-1960) fourth from left, and William (Bill) Warne (c.1872-1921), in dark clothing and soft hat, sixth from left. Both Harry and Freddy worked at Golden Dagger Mine in the 1920s. In the census taken on 2 April 1911 Henry, described as a 'Tin Miner' and 'Hewer Underground', was living at the Temperance Hotel (now the East Dart) in Postbridge. This had been taken over by his brother Solomon and wife Mabel the year before. Brother Frank and sister Rebecca also lived there, together with tin miner Albert George Coaker. Extraordinarily, New Zealander and nuclear physicist Ernest Rutherford was also staying there that night, with his wife Mary, as well as eminent physicist Charles Galton Darwin, who was the grandson of Charles Darwin, plus Hilda Johnstone, a medieval historian from Manchester University, and others.[209] William Warne was Captain of Vitifer Mine, taking over from John Webb. Tragically he was killed in an accident involving a horse and cart at Dartmeet in 1921.[210]

Second from left is John Sowden, an older miner. He is remembered as being a regular 'chapel' man. He is thought to have come from Cornwall and to have lived at both Pizwell and Mardon near Moretonhampstead.[211]

Second from right is William Herbert (Bert) White (c.1882-1928) who was from a farming family of Lower Merripit, Postbridge. In 1908 he married Ethel Jory (1882-1975) the daughter of Capt. Richard Jory. In the census of 1901 Ethel was described as a 'dressmaker'. Bert's sister married Ethel's brother William. Bert himself was tragically killed aged 46 when he got off his cart to pick something off the road and was struck from behind by a car driven by a chauffeur to Lord Illingworth, where there is a 'little bit of a pinch' (i.e. rising ground) between Statts Bridge and the top of Merripit Hill.[212]

On the right is Lewis Evely (1886-1971) of Hullacombe, Whiddon Down. He would have to leave home at 4am on Monday mornings to reach the mine, some eight miles distant, sometimes walking with Dick Lentern. He took food with him, including tins of condensed milk, bacon and butter. He courted Marina Hill of Shilstone Farm, Throwleigh, who he married in 1910 and was able to shorten his journey somewhat by living there for twelve months. He would cycle to the mine from the farm, taking a reed basket with a lid, containing, bread, bacon, pasties, tea, sugar etc. The couple then moved to a rented cottage at Hobhouse, Whiddon Down.[213] He appears in a photograph of church leaders in 1906.[214] He and his wife emigrated to America in 1914 and were in mid-Atlantic when the First World War broke out. They settled in Utah where

he worked in salt mines. In 1918 he moved to Detroit and worked for both Chrysler and Ford. His letters home were 'full of religion'.[215]

He also appears in Fig. 68, kneeling on the right. These are undoubtedly Vitifer miners, but the location of the photograph has not been established, as they are on a good road outside an unidentified building. Harry Warne is standing on the left and John Sowden on the right. The tallest standing man might well be Frank Rounsfell who was living at Dinah's Cottage, Golden Dagger in 1911 with his wife Eliza and 2-month old daughter Gladys. Frank was born in Nottingham in about 1883 and appears in the iconic group of miners outside the adit level at Golden Dagger (Fig. 100).

Kneeling on the left is Harry Westcott (1861-1932) of Rixhill near Tavistock. Born in North Molton and a cobbler and harness-maker by trade, he married a girl from Chudleigh but took up mining. With several companions he used to walk weekly to and from Vitifer, a distance of 14 miles as the crow flies, but eventually they acquired a pony and trap for the journey. He was blind in one eye. His teenage son, also called Harry, worked with him, but died in India during the First World War.[216]

Another miner was Herbert Leaman (born 1884) (Fig. 69) of Dury Farm, Postbridge. Annie Leaman, his sister, recalled that he worked at Vitifer for about nine years until about 1908 when he left because of a bronchial complaint ('Miners' Disease'). He worked underground as a trammer and recalled that the mine was warm and wet. He was paid £1 per week when he first went to the mine.[217]

William Bickell (Bill) Jory (c.1877-1927) was the eldest son of Captain Richard and Anna Jory. He is recorded as a tin dresser at Vitifer in the census of 1901 and took over from his father as Captain of Vitifer Mine for a while, and also as Captain of Golden Dagger Mine for a while after the death of John James Coaker in 1913. His wife was Bessie White, a Postbridge farmer's daughter (Fig. 70). In about 1916 the family moved to Delaware Road, Gunnislake and he worked at Clitters Mine before moving to Kit Hill Mine where he was Captain.[218] He also appears in Fig. 100.

69. Herbert Leaman, tin miner. *Photographer not known*

70. William Jory with his wife Bessie and daughter Winnie. *Photographer not known, ex R. White.*

71. South Zeal
miners who worked
at Vitifer –
LEFT:
Jack Hellier,
RIGHT:
Dick Lentern,
CENTRE:
John Osborn,
Bottom:
Will Tucker.
*Photographer not
known*

Several men who worked at Ramsley copper mine on the north-eastern edge of Dartmoor found work at Vitifer when Ramsley closed in 1909 (Fig. 71). Among them was John (Jack) Hellier (1854-1927) of Sticklepath who had been an underground 'Captain' at Ramsley. He was born in the Drewe Arms, Drewsteignton and married a Miss Burgoyne who had been born in the Oxenham Arms, South Zeal! He was already aged 55 when Ramsley closed, and then walked to Vitifer from Sticklepath, lodging at the Warren House Inn. He told his grandson that his damp clothes would sometimes freeze overnight. He was superstitious, considering a robin tapping at the window to be a bad omen.[219] John James Osborn of South Zeal (born c.1865 in Sourton), and three of his sons – Ernest, Otto and Will – all worked at the Postbridge mines before the First World War and later at the Kolar Gold Fields in India.[220] They walked across the moor together, crossing the R. Teign above Chagford. Apparently, they sometimes caught trout with dynamite en route![221] Richard (Dick) Lentern of South Zeal and Will ('Bobby') Tucker (1886-1950) of South Zeal also worked at the Postbridge mines.[222] His father

72. Moses Bawden.
Photographer not known, ex Henrietta Morgan

Aubrey had done the same and travelled across the moor with a friend – they had a pony between them and adopted the 'ride and tied' method, whereby one rode ahead and the other walked. After a certain distance the one riding tethered the pony and started walking, enabling the other to reach the pony, catch up and overtake, and so repeat the process.[223]

Of special significance in the later story of the Postbridge mines is Moses Bawden (1834-1916) (Fig. 72) who had connections with them from the 1860s. He was born in Camborne into a mining family.[224] With other partners, he acquired Birch Tor & Vitifer mine in 1868, and within a few years it was 'entirely' in his hands. He obtained a lease of the sett for thirty-one years from 29 September 1887 and it remained under his management at a very low level of activity until 1902 when he sold the lease.[225] He also managed Golden Dagger Mine at much the same time, and invested thousands of pounds there.

Ethel White (née Jory in 1882) remembered him as 'a 'ansom man'. He visited the mine once a month and would have a leg of mutton cooked by her mother (Anna Jory) – the children would be given the leftovers.[226] As a child Elsie Bellamy (née Coaker in 1896) was impressed by his

73. Moses Bawden's Bungalow, King's Oven, 1976.
T. Greeves

74. 'Cape Horn'
(West Bungalow/
West Cottages)
about 1910.
*Chapman & Son
11726*

'beautiful white beard', and his upright bearing and described him as 'a
dear old gent'.[227] Nellie White (née Sleep in 1896) reckoned he 'brought
more work to Postbridge than anybody else'.[228]

A timber-framed bungalow (Fig. 73) near the Warren House Inn was
probably built by him in about 1875. It was always known as Bawden's
Bungalow or King's Oven Bungalow. His daughter Mabel Terdrey Stiff
was consumptive and lived in it for a time. He himself stayed there when
he came out to the mine from Tavistock to pay wages each month, and
would keep his pony in a stable at the back.[229]

Another, larger, bungalow (Fig. 74) of similar date was on the south
side of the road towards Postbridge. This was officially known as West
Cottages but local people always knew it as 'Cape Horn' because of its
exposed location. It was lived in by miners, including Richard and Anna
Jory in retirement (Fig. 75).

75. Richard and
Anna Jory.
*Photographer not
known, ex R. White*

76. Warren House
Inn with carriage
outside.
*Photographer not
known*

The Warren House Inn (Fig. 76), built in 1845, was a key venue for
the miners from both Vitifer and Golden Dagger. Its predecessor, New
House, on the opposite side of the road, probably served miners from at
least the mid-eighteenth century.[230] The diversity of the workforce
sometimes led to confrontation. Blacksmith George Leaman remembered
it was 'as if a pig was being killed up there' sometimes.[231]

One miner, who actually acquired a licence of tin ground adjoining
Birch Tor & Vitifer in 1867-8[232], was Samuel Oldridge (1836-1899) from
Lewannick in Cornwall. He married Jane Warne on 1 November 1858 in
Ashburton, daughter of the publican Joseph Warne and his wife Elizabeth
(Fig. 77). In the 1870s Samuel worked at Steeperton Tor Mine,[233] for
which he also obtained licences in 1875-6, but by the mid-1880s was
living in Gateshead, Durham and then in Barrow-in-Furness, Lancashire.
He died in Co. Durham.[234] His sons Mark and Joseph were also miners.

The landlord for nearly forty years spanning the late nineteenth and
early twentieth centuries was Tommy Hext (Fig. 78) with his wife

80

Elizabeth who seems to have actually held the tenancy. Born at Hartyland, Postbridge in about 1846, he stood about 6ft 2in and had a long beard which he was fond of stroking. Beer and cider were kept in barrels at the back and Mrs Hext would shuffle out to get your order. Beer was 2½d a pint, an ounce of tobacco 3½d and a port and lemon 2½d.[235] Some miners had a prodigious capacity for drink, consuming as much as sixteen pints. Ale would be heated in a funnel in the fireplace.[236]

Not everyone found the influence of the Warren House Inn beneficial. Mr Cressacre George Moor was an experienced mining man, an author of respected mining

77. Samuel and Jane Oldridge and family. *Photographer not known, ex Bob Cowan*

78. Tommy Hext, landlord of Warren House Inn 1883-c.1920. *Photographer not known, ex Audrey Mortimore*

FIELD SANITATION

BY
C. G. MOOR,
CAPTAIN 1ST LONDON SANITARY COMPANY R.A.M.C. (T.); M.A., CANTAB., F.I.C., F.C.S.,
MEMBER OF THE SOCIETY OF PUBLIC ANALYSTS; ASSOCIATE OF THE
INSTITUTE OF MINING AND METALLURGY; PUBLIC
ANALYST, DORSET, POOLE AND PENZANCE;
LATE SENIOR DEMONSTRATOR PUBLIC HEALTH LABORATORIES,
KING'S COLLEGE, LONDON

AND
E. A. COOPER,
CAPTAIN 1ST LONDON SANITARY COMPANY R.A.M.C. (T.); D.SC., LOND.; FORMERLY
BEIT MEMORIAL RESEARCH FELLOW; A.R.C.S., LONDON;
RESEARCH FELLOW, LISTER INSTITUTE

LONDON
BAILLIÈRE, TINDALL AND COX
8, HENRIETTA STREET, COVENT GARDEN
1918

TIN MINING

A COMPLETE GUIDE FOR ALL ACTIVELY
INTERESTED OR ENGAGED IN TIN MINING

BY
C. G. MOOR, M.A. (Cantab.)
FELLOW OF THE INSTITUTE OF CHEMISTRY; FELLOW OF THE CHEMICAL
SOCIETY; MEMBER OF THE CORNISH INSTITUTE OF ENGINEERS
AUTHOR OF "THE RECOGNITION OF MINERALS"

LONDON
SIR ISAAC PITMAN & SONS, LTD.
PARKER STREET, KINGSWAY, W.C.2
BATH, MELBOURNE, TORONTO, NEW YORK
1928

79. Title pages of two books by Cressacre George Moor.

manuals (Fig. 79) and a technical advisor to Golden Dagger Mine at about the time of the First World War. He complained (seemingly without justification) to the Duchy that Mrs Hext was allowing miners to become inebriated.[237]

A report by Josiah Paull, written for John Taylor & Sons, following a visit on 6 June 1914, gives some valuable detail of buildings, plant and underground activity:

> The buildings consisted of a '9 room bungalow, Office and Store adjoining with two rooms over. Caretakers cottage with similar cottage adjoining, a building for accommodation of miners to give sleeping accommodation to 16 men, Smithy, miners changing house with drying tube and a peat store at end of same, carpenters shop, stable and trap house.' The Mill consisted of '16 Cornish Stamps driven by Water Wheel 40 feet dia. by 5 feet breast, Luhrig classifiers, 3 Buss tables for coarse product from classifiers and two round buddles for the fine product. Final dressing house contains two round and one square buddle, tie [=tye], tossing kieves with packing gear, scales, tin hutch etc. There is also a drying oven for drying concentrates with a Wetherel type two pole Electro Magnetic Separator for removing Specular Iron from the concentrates...the iron is removed easily by this Separator and leaves a very high grade tin product which commands top prices at the ticketing...[A] small turbine is used for generating electricity for lighting, magnetic separation etc...'

82

Of some estimated 22 lodes, several were named as having been worked on – from south to north: Scudley, Elvan, Coronation, D, A, Lances, Wall Shaft, Hambly's, New Shaft or North Lode. Engine Shaft on the Wall Shaft Lode had been sunk 70 fathoms (420 ft/128m) below adit level.

Work done by the present company since 1903 had been

'confined to an Adit level driven east on the A. [sic = D.] Lode, the total length of the Adit being about 1,300 feet. At about 900 feet from the mouth a crosscut has been driven North to the A. Lode and South to Coronation, Elvan and the Scudley Lodes. The A. Lode is the widest lode varying from 2 to 4 feet but contains little tin and in consequence of this was only driven on a short distance. The D. Lode previous to the last 12 months has been the chief producer and about 100 tons of black tin has been recovered from here and from what information I can gather the ore yielded about 20 lbs. of tin to the ton. The payable portion of the lode is practically worked out above Adit to near the present end. The walls of the lodes are generally soft decomposed granite and East of the Crosscut mentioned these have caved so that the end of the Adit on D. Lode is now inaccessible. Below Adit on this lode 3 winzes have been sunk, the deepest being 60 feet, but I understand the low tin values found, combined with the water met with being more than the hand pumps could deal with, led to work below the Adit being abandoned.'

The Coronation Lode reached by the southern crosscut was

'a hard quartz lode 1 foot wide containing 14 lbs. of tin to the ton'.

Further south the Elvan Lode, another hard quartz lode averaging 2 ft wide, was intersected and driven east and west for 238 ft, but was not considered payable and was abandoned. The most southerly lode was the Scudley Lode which was driven east and west of the crosscut for 131 ft and 85 ft respectively. In June 1914 its east end was being driven on a lode 2 ft 6 in wide.

'The lode has been stoped above the level for some 140 feet in length and for a height [of] about 30 feet. Two men were stoping here at the time of my visit...Most of the tin sold during the past 11 months has been recovered from this lode and...the value has been from 18 to 20 lbs. black tin to the ton. The encasing rock immediately next to the lode is a soft decomposed granite and does not permit open stopes. To prevent caving it is necessary to stope on one side of the lode, using such stuff for filling, and then take the lode out separately...'

Josiah Paull concluded that, 'I do not consider the property would prove remunerative to a large Company' but 'a company with a small capital', prepared to expend £5,000-£6,000 on waterpower and reopening the Deep Adit, 'would get a fair return for their outlay'.[238]

However, the impact of the First World War caused the mine to close. The *Cornish Chamber of Mines Yearbook 1919* recorded that it was 'a private company owning the Birch Tor and Vitifer Mines' and that 'Owing to shortage of labour, operations have been suspended since 1914'.[239]

These bald words do not quite reflect circumstances on the mine itself during the War, as a workforce was still retained, with some surface activity, in aid of the 'war effort'. For example, Philip Crosby Pope, a consulting engineer, was employed as manager for a time. His daughter recalled living in a wooden bungalow 'right on the mine'. Match-boarding separated the rooms, most of which were 'opening one out of the other'. Cooking was Perfection Oil Cooker. There was some night work, lit by 'arc lamps', which led to 'a very foolish lady' reporting suspicious activity to the police, who were obliged to visit the mine to interview her father as a 'suspected spy'! He was able to satisfy them entirely.[240]

Work continued in the immediate post-War period by the company titled Birch Tor & Vitifer Ltd. Few details of activity have yet come to light, but a copy of accounts for the year ending 30 April 1920 indicate that a total of £26,299 10s 4½d had already been expended by the company on plant, machinery etc. Costs for the year 1919-1920 totalled £494 4s 10½d of which labour was £281 18s. Sales of tin had raised £140 14s 2d. The Revenue Account Balance was £1,562 15s 4½d.[241]

The company went into liquidation in late 1922.[242] A new lease was granted by the Duchy of Cornwall to Dartmoor Tin Mines Ltd on 1 March 1923, for a period of twenty-one years.[243] This was jointly for Birch Tor & Vitifer and Golden Dagger, but it seems that it was the latter mine that became the main focus of any work in the remainder of the 1920s, and the Vitifer complex was, essentially, abandoned.

VITIFER MINE – BACK TO THE LAND

The appearance of some of the buildings at Vitifer around the time of its abandonment in the 1920s were captured by artists Edward T. Holding and Edward Massforth Neatby (Figs 80 & 81). Holding's image seems to have some artistic licence in the detailed appearance of the buildings, but Neatby's accomplished work is the best image of the Dry

80. Watercolour of mine buildings by Edward T. Holding about 1920. *ex Stephen Woods*

81. Watercolour of Dry by Edward Massforth Neatby 1929. *Milton, 2006, Plate XV, ex Brian Le Messurier*

82. Stamps
waterwheel about
1929.
*Ealing Studio/Studio
Canal Ltd*

83. Waterwheel
and stamps, early
1930s. *Cliff Goss*

yet known. Despite the fact that the Miners' House was refurbished by Donald Smith in the late 1920s, most of the buildings at Vitifer soon became roofless and derelict, and were certainly in this state by 1930.

However, the waterwheel and dressing floors at SX 68328071 remained intact for some time and were fortunately photographed in the making of the film 'Escape' in about 1929 by Ealing Studios (Fig. 82). This was based on John Galsworthy's successful play of the same name premiered in 1926. Figs 83-86 show the waterwheel and stamps in various states of abandonment in the 1930s. The

84. Stamps waterwheel about 1935. *Photographer not known, ex W. Dodd*

85. Waterwheel and stamps from mine track April 1937. *John Rawlins*

86. Stamps waterwheel April 1937. *John Rawlins*

87. Dressing floors,
28 August 1937.
P. H. G. Richardson

88. Ruins of mine
buildings about
1930.
*Ealing Studio/Studio
Canal Ltd*

man climbing on the wheel in Fig. 84 is W. Dodd (born 1912) of
Chagford. He and others noted that the cast-iron frame of the wheel had
the maker's name on it – PEARCE of TAVISTOCK.[244] The totally ruined
dressing floors were recorded by Peter Richardson on 28 August 1937
(Fig. 87).

The further gradual decay of the mine buildings in the 1930s is shown
in Figs 88-92. In Fig. 93 Miss Beatrice ('Beatie') Warne and her fiancé

89. Ruins of mine buildings, April 1937. *John Rawlins*

90. Stack of Vitifer 'Dry', April 1937. *John Rawlins*

91. Pipework at
Vitifer, April 1937.
John Rawlins

Stanley Brook are seen by a Vitifer bungalow in about 1933. Beatie
(1913-2010) was the daughter of Harry and Polly Warne and lived in
several of the mine dwellings at both Vitifer and Golden Dagger in her
childhood and young adulthood.[245]

By the 1950s collapse of nearly all features was well advanced though
the stack of the Dry still survived as a key landmark (Figs 94-5). Today
only foundations remain, apart from some courses of walling of the
Carpenter's Shop.

92. Beatie Warne
by ruins of mine
buildings about
1933. *Photographer
not known*

93. Stanley Brook and Beatie Warne by Vitifer bungalow, about 1933. *Photographer not known*

94. Vitifer from site of turbine house, with stack for Dry, and ruins of Carpenter's Shop, 16 May 1952. *P. H. G. Richardson*

95. Stack for Dry at Vitifer, etc 1950s. *Photographer not known*

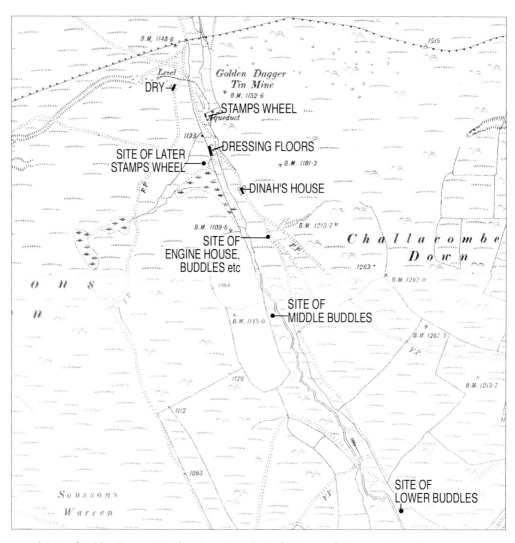

96. Map of Golden Dagger Mine based on OS 2nd edn 6-inch, 1906, Sheets 99NE & SE (not to scale)

GOLDEN DAGGER MINE

With its wondrously evocative name, this mine has a special place in the story of Dartmoor tinworking as it was the last to be in commercial work, until November 1930, and even saw some activity shortly before the start of the Second World War.

Its name is unique and is likely to relate to some interesting discovery, quite possibly of some prehistoric artefact in a burial cairn disturbed by miners. The earliest known record of the name takes us as far back as 1851[246] which is more than twenty years before the discovery of a Bronze Age dagger pommel decorated with tiny gold pins, from a cairn at Two Barrows on Hameldown. I have been told that the Black Prince had once lost a golden dagger at the mine, but cannot give this any reliable credence.

We are on safer ground when speculating about early tinworking here. Streamworks in the valley and its tributaries are likely to be of medieval or even earlier date. The great east-west openwork, centred at SX 680803 on the west side of the valley, in which later shafts were sunk and adits driven, may very well also be medieval in origin. Supporting evidence for lodeworking in this area in perhaps the sixteenth century, takes the form of a fine granite 'mortarstone' on which tin ore was crushed by water-powered stamps, which was found somewhere at Golden Dagger in the 1920s (Fig. 97). When the mine closed in 1930 Mr Philip Stanhope had it moved to his property at Stone, Widecombe, where it still is.

On the west side of the sett, close to the Wallabrook, at SX 673799 is a stamping mill and dressing floor typical of the years around 1800.[247]

The mine office and Captain's residence from the late nineteenth century onwards was known as Dinah's House/Cottage/Bungalow at SX 685800. At least from the early years of the nineteenth

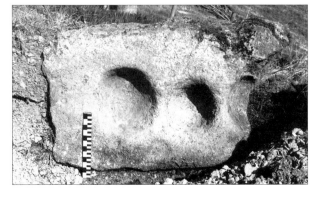

97. Triple mortarstone for crushing tin ore of 16th/17th century found at Golden Dagger in 1920s, at Stone, Widecombe in 1976. Scale: 30cm/12in.
T. Greeves

93

98. Stamps
waterwheel,
Golden Dagger
Mine at SX 6839
8027, about 1900.
*Photographer not
known, ex Graham
Amhof*

century there were stamping mills at, or very near to, this site. A cottage, known as Stamps Cottage, is referred to from at least 1841. In 1851 members of the Gilbert family from St Hilary in Cornwall were living there.[248] The name by which it was known in the twentieth century is perhaps most likely to be derived from Dinah Hext who was living at Stamps Cottage at the time of the censuses of 1861 and 1871.[249]

The mine was clearly working on a significant scale early in 1851 as in May of that year it sold 2½ tons of black tin to the Calenick Smelting House in Cornwall, at £50 10s per ton. [250]

Moses Bawden first became involved in the mine in 1879 and is said to have spent £20,000 there over the next twenty-five years or so, employing a significant workforce of up to forty-one persons.[251]

The trauma of a rare fatal accident at the mine was still remembered by Louise Warne (née French c.1879) when I met her in August 1972. She always knew that a man called Stephens had died at Golden Dagger when she was small, and her younger brother Sidney French knew that he was called Dick Stephens.[252] The young man in question was Richard Henry Stephens and he was killed in an explosion underground in February 1882, after recklessly using an iron bar to 'tamp' (i.e. ram home) the charge of powder into a bored hole, when working with John Webb. He was fearfully injured and doctors were summoned from Moretonhampstead and Chagford but neither was able to attend. Another doctor from Moretonhampstead, Mr May, demanded receipt of a fee beforehand and also failed to respond, which was much criticised by the coroner.[253]

A massively broad waterwheel working sixteen heads of stamps at SX 68398027 (Fig. 98) is likely to have been installed during this period of activity as the original photograph was annotated by hand, somewhat inaccurately, as 'Bordon's [i.e. Bawden's] Copper Stamp on Dartmoor'.[254] The indistinct site can be found on the east side of the Redwater stream and unusually had a launder approaching the wheel at right-angles.

The only underground photograph of Golden Dagger Mine so far known is shown in Fig. 99. It gives a good impression of conditions that

99. Underground scene at Golden Dagger Mine. *Chapman & Son 11941*

95

must have prevailed for centuries on Dartmoor, with great beams of timber keeping the sidewalls apart and roof in place, besides providing a base for working platforms. It could well illustrate words written of the Dartmoor tinner in about 1590 by John Hooker: *His lyffe most commonly is in pyttes and caves under the grounde of a greate depth and in great daunger because the earthe above his hedd is in sundry places crossed and posted over with tymber to keepe the same from fallinge.*[255] Men are seen working at two levels. Running vertically down the centre of the image is a dark vein of tin ore about 12 inches /30cm wide. The miner in the foreground holding an iron bar is 'Cape Horn' George Coaker, brother to Captain 'John James'.

Sidney French (1889-1976) of Postbridge had fond memories of working here before the First World War:

'I used to like Dagger. Dagger Mine was a nice little mine to work in...We were up there working, up Dagger. Us didn't go in the level, we went up the gully and went down a little shaft, a little air shaft, and 'twasn't very deep down and we had a lode there...and he was solid, he was solid with tin, and us worked there, oh I don't know, for a brave old while. Me and me brother [Dick French], us was one shift, and Freddy [Warne] and Jack Webb they was other shift, and Jimmy... he was the boss there then to Dagger. Us used to go in for so long then us used to come out to the floors and clean up the tin. There wasn't very many of us there, just eight or nine of us, I think. Us was there for a brave bit like that. Then this yer lode he got runned out or he wasn't so good...But he was a lovely little lode for some time. Solid tin he was.'[256]

When Sidney French first worked underground at Golden Dagger, the miners had to walk up to the Dry at Vitifer, half a mile up the valley, to change their clothes. Sidney French commented,

'Some places it was wet, some places it was warm. And you'd come out from underground sometimes all wet and hot and before you could get up to the Dry – 'twas a long ways up from where us used to come out from the level – you'd take off your coat and he'd stand up, freezed through. It takes a bit of believing but is quite right...You'd be in there, you'd be hot, sweating and all that. When you come out...you'd be going right up against the wind.'[257]

Underground men wore flannel shirts and jackets called 'slops' made of material called 'Rushin' Duck', which was 'like a very fine canvas'. It would swell with the wet and was very tough wearing. The trousers were also known as 'Ducks'. Some men wore 'Yorks' tied below the knee to give looseness to the knee if bending or kneeling. A pair of working boots cost 9s 9d. Tallow candles – 'green, with a fairly big wick on them' – were stuck in lumps of clay on hats, and tobacco was smoked in clay pipes.[258]

In about 1911 the Dartmoor Mineral Company Ltd were occupiers of a cottage and mine at Golden Dagger. The owner was Sir Harry Eve, a

senior judge, who at one time threatened to blow up the adit in a dispute with the Duchy of Cornwall regarding water.[259] The mine had 'Magazine & store. Smithy, offices. Mill & tin floors'. The workings covered an area of 25 acres, and the gross value of the mine was £590.[260]

Chapman & Son of Dawlish published an iconic image of miners at Golden Dagger (Fig. 100) at this time, and whoever took and printed the photograph should have been highly pleased by its superlative quality. This happens to be the first photograph of Dartmoor tin miners that I was shown – by Annie Sleep of Postbridge in August 1970.

Eleven miners are posed outside the adit entrance at SX 68228037 with a tram wagon on rails – these led down to the stamps wheel seen in Fig. 98. The men have mostly been identified with confidence. From left to right they are:

* Frank Rounsfell who was living at Dinah's Cottage in 1911, aged 29, with his 25-year old wife Eliza and their two-month old daughter Gladys. Eliza had been born in Ashburton, but Frank was born in Nottingham in about 1882.[261]

* Johnny (Jack) Wills of Ashburton (with pick raised).[262]

* Bill Crout (??) of Buckfast.

100. Miners outside Golden Dagger Mine adit. *Chapman & Son 11937*

* William Jory (1877-1927). He was the son of Captain Richard Jory of Vitifer and took over from him there for a while, as he also did at Golden Dagger, where he took over as Captain from John James Coaker (no.11) on his death in 1912. In about 1916 he moved to east Cornwall and worked in mines there.[263]

* William Henry (Harry) Earland (with folded arms, and in bowler hat). He was the mine blacksmith and carpenter, but was not local, having been born in about 1867 in Broadwoodkelly.[264]

* 'Cape Horn' George Coaker, brother of John James Coaker (no.11) and cousin of George Coaker (no.9). He also appears in Fig. 99.

* Charlie Rowlands (c.1892-1967). He was an orphan from Plymouth, brought to Postbridge by Mr Balkwill, a chemist, who acquired the lease of Lydgate in 1893.[265] He continued working at Golden Dagger in the 1920s. Unusually, in May 1926, he placed a formal apology for an unspecified misdemeanour, to Miss Lena Stephens of the Warren House Inn in a local newspaper.[266] He died in 1967 at the age of seventy-five.[267]

* Unknown, but from Ashburton.

* George Coaker of Postbridge, the son of Jonas Coaker of Pizwell. He was the cousin of George Coaker (no.6).

* Sam Withycombe of Postbridge. He had sons John (see Fig. 103) and William.

* John James Coaker (1873-1913). The son of John Coaker of 'Cape Horn', and brother to George (no.6), he was always known as John James. He married Mary, the daughter of Captain Richard and Anna

101. Stamps waterwheel, Golden Dagger Mine, about 1912. *Chapman & Son 11938*

Jory of Vitifer, and was Captain of Golden Dagger Mine when this photograph was taken. He died at Dinah's House in 1913 at the age of forty, suffering from pneumonia, which was a relatively common complaint among miners.[268]

102. Cornish stamps, Golden Dagger Mine about 1912. *Chapman & Son 11939*

The adit was the scene of a lucky escape for the miners, when water burst out of flooded old workings without warning. Sidney French was an eyewitness to what happened:

> 'Well, Harold Jory and an old man called Sowden, us was there working, and we were out having our lunch, or crib as we called it...We were in the Dry where us used to dry our clothes. We heard something, and I was the first one to jump up and get to the door. And when I opened the door...the water was going down. And us had great poles there, oh, so big around as meself, what us used to put in in underground as timber where it was soft ground...[It] washed they away, yes.'[269]

Elsie Bellamy (née Coaker), daughter of John James Coaker, captain of the mine, remembered him sending a telegram to London after the wash-out, saying the men would be off work for a few days.[270]

From the adit, tin ore was taken to the stamps, initially those seen in Fig. 98. But this very wheel seems to have been refurbished and moved early in the 1900s to a new position a few hundred yards further down the valley at SX 68348012 (Fig. 101). The wheel was 22½ ft in diameter x 9ft breast (6.9m x 2.7m)[271] and very powerful. It operated sixteen heads of Cornish stamps (Fig. 102), housed in a large galvanised shed. The massive

103. Round buddle and boys, Golden Dagger Mine. *Chapman & Son* *11942*

iron axle is clearly visible as are the projecting cams which engaged in sequence with vertical lifters (seen behind the axle) thus raising the stamp heads which, as the axle turned, then dropped onto the ore, crushing it to a fine sand. Holes of oval section can also be seen in the stamps axle – these were used for retrieving broken cams which themselves were set in holes of rectangular section.[272] The man in the photograph may well be George Soper, who also operated stamps at Hexworthy Mine and, later, the turbine there. He was deaf, which may well have been a consequence of working in such a noisy environment. He also stammered and did not have full use of his right arm.[273] Sidney French recalled that there were two shifts for the stamps men: 7am-5pm and 5pm-7am. The horizontal strips at the bottom of the boxes into which the crushed material fell could be removed if access was needed for repair or cleaning.[274]

Fig. 103 is a particularly informative image of a round buddle at Golden Dagger, at dressing floors at SX 68398015, on the righthand side of the track down to Dinah's House, and now completely swamped by scrub and bog vegetation. This type of buddle was introduced to Dartmoor in the mid-nineteenth century. The photograph clearly shows the wooden launder which fed crushed tin ore and water onto the central

100

cone. From the base of the cone, a deposit was built up on a gently sloping surface, so that the heaviest and best quality tin settled closest to the central cone. Revolving arms or 'sweeps', with pieces of rag or tin sack hanging from them, were powered by gearing driven by a small waterwheel, and ensured an even deposit was built up to a depth of about 12 inches (300mm) maximum, with tin catching against slight 'riffles' created on the surface.[275] The arms are not visible in this photograph as they have been removed so that the three boys can dig out the deposit, once the tin dresser has graded it into 'heads, middles and tails' by scoring circles with his shovel. The tails have already been cleared by the boy on the right; the boy on the left has his shovel poised on the middles, and the boy second left has his shovel resting on the heads. The buddle boys, from left to right, are:

* Reginald (Reggie) James Coaker (1898-1918). He was the son of John James Coaker, and died of wounds on the Somme on 22 September 1918. He served in the Devonshire Regiment as a Private and is buried in Grave 10, Row AA, Plot XV in the Villers-Bretonneux cemetery.[276]

* Sidney Warne (c.1897-1917). He was the son of George and Mary Warne of Archerton Cottage, and was killed on 11 May 1917, aged twenty, probably in the Battle of Arras. His body was never identified.[277]

* John Withycombe. He was the son of Sam Withycombe (Fig. 100). He eventually moved to a farm in Staffordshire where he died in about 1969.[278]

Cressacre George Moor was an interesting character connected with Golden Dagger from November 1909, when he is named in a printed Memorandum of Association for The Golden Dagger Mine Limited. The Capital of the Company was £5000.[279] Fig. 104 is of a postcard written by

104. Postcard sent to Capt Wm Jory 1914 from C. G. Moor.

105. Postcard sent
to Master Meeks
1914

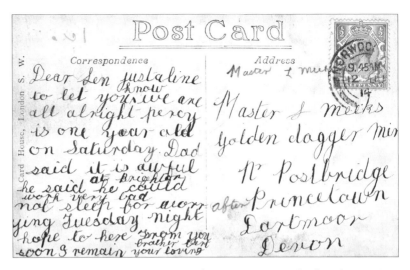

him to Captain William Jory in 1914 when he was involved with tin mines
in Nigeria. Apart from being a tin prospector and adventurer, C. G.Moor
was a chemist and public analyst for Exeter, Dorset and Penzance. He was
also the author of *The Recognition of Minerals* (1909), *Tin Mining* (1928), and
of several other books on chemical analysis and even *Field Sanitation* (1918).
In the 1920s and 1930s he was working the Excelsior Mine on Kit Hill,
Cornwall,[280] while also having an interest in the Ashanti Goldfields in
Ghana (then Gold Coast)[281]. His manner was 'refined...almost...courtly'
according to Peter Richardson.[282] Elsie Bellamy (née Coaker) remembered
him staying at Dinah's House at Golden Dagger.[283]

Fig. 105 is of a card sent to Leonard Meeks from his brother Frank in
1914. The Meeks family was from Upper Norwood in south-east London
and Leonard (born c.1901) was the eldest of four sons, but why he was at
Golden Dagger Mine is as yet unknown.[284]

Little is yet known of detailed activity at Golden Dagger between
about 1918-1925. In October 1922 assays of tin samples were made by G.
T. Holloway & Co, 13 Emmett St, Limehouse, E14 for Dartmoor Tin
Mines Ltd.,[285] but the company went into liquidation in 1923. However,
Albert Flewin (c.1854-c.1929), who is said to have trained at the
Camborne School of Mines, moved to Vitifer/Golden Dagger in about
1919 as manager, with his Swiss wife Marie. They had previously been at
Pensilva in Cornwall where he had managed at least two mines in the
Caradon area, including East Caradon Mine 1907-8. He also worked
mines at St Neot 1908-1910.[286]

At Golden Dagger he is said to have employed just five or six men,
working on the surface only, one of whom was almost certainly Harry
Warne.[287] Directors of the mine occasionally travelled to
Moretonhampstead and held meetings in the White Hart Hotel.[288]

102

Albert Flewin, who had 'baleful blue eyes'[289] was long ago described to me as a 'right arum-scarum'[290] and was considered rather self-important, often carrying a vanning shovel around with him. At one time he travelled to Redruth to buy some equipment and in the hope of attracting cheap Cornish labour for 30s per week.[291] In the early 1930s his widow became a resident housekeeper in Exeter for Edmund Meek Slatter of Great Rock Mine[292] and received £100 in his will of 1933.[293]

Their son William (Bill) Flewin (1903-2001) was born at Pensilva on 1 January 1903. Not long after the First World War he was based in army barracks at Bristol where he was trained to ride a motorcycle with a machine gun attached. He quite frequently had periods of leave and would ride down to his parents at Golden Dagger. On one of his early visits, in about 1920, he extended electricity from the turbine at Vitifer down to Dinah's House by carrying a cable on poles down the valley – there was one positive wire and one negative wire. He thus enabled his mother to purchase an electric stove, when previously only paraffin was available![294] In 1926 he married Winifred Lock of Wareham (Fig. 106). In 1996 at the age of ninety-three he walked down and back to Dinah's House from the Warren House Inn (see Fig. 10).

106. Wedding of Bill Flewin to Winifred Lock about 1927. *Photographer not known*

Shortly before Christmas 1925 a young man aged only eighteen arrived at Golden Dagger Mine from Moretonhampstead Station, as a passenger in a Wolseley Ten Tourer driven by Jack ('Jan Buzz') Withycombe of Soussons Farm. His name was Donald Langley ('Longboy') Smith (1907-1993) and he had never been to Dartmoor before. He was born on 22 June 1907 in the Jolly Miller public house in King's Langley in Hertfordshire, which was owned by his father Albert E. Smith.

An entrepreneur aunt of his had arranged for him to become electrical and mechanical engineer at Golden Dagger Mine, having introduced Flewin to Hyram J. Cattaneo, Chairman of Torr Trust Ltd. which had taken over the mine in February 1925. Donald had been working in London as an electrician for Maunsell Odlin, especially on lighting for Strand Electric for West End theatres.

He first spent about six weeks from October 1925 at Petters of Yeovil learning about diesel engines, and then travelled to Dartmoor with one of their engineers, a Mr Penny. One of their engines, costing about £400,[295] was to be installed at Golden Dagger.

It was 'as cold as charity', with snow piled up on either side of the road. Donald thought, 'What on earth have I let myself in for?'[296] The Flewins were in Dinah's House and were constantly arguing. Mrs Flewin was 'quite pleasant', but Flewin was a 'most irascible type'. The next day Donald was introduced to the workforce whom he thought were a 'rough looking crowd'. Harry Warne was the first of them he met. Another was George Austin who walked daily to and from Moretonhampstead, arriving for work at 8am. It was he who said to Donald, 'You hate it now, but you won't want to leave it when the time comes'.[297] For Donald, that Christmas was the most miserable he had ever spent, gazing out of his bedroom window onto the bleak snow-covered slope of Challacombe Down. The jug of water had frozen in his bedroom.[298]

But all was to change and, thanks to his ingenuity and skills, within two years he was actually managing the mine. It is almost entirely thanks to him that the mine kept going as long as it did, until November 1930.

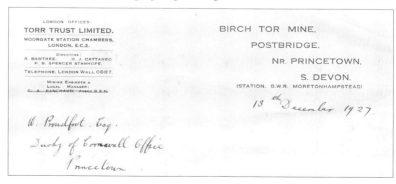

107. Torr Trust Limited letterhead for Birch Tor Mine

In February 1925 the mine had been taken over by Torr Trust Limited (Fig. 107). Directors were H. J. Cattaneo (Chairman), Thomas L. Davies (Secretary), R. Bawtree, and two others.

The Flewins left the mine in 1926 and C.A. Panchaud took over as manager. Fig. 108 shows the workforce outside Dinah's House in 1927. Standing from left to right are:

* Lilian Kate Trude (born 1899), wife of Harry
* Donald Smith (1907-1993)
* Walter/Walt ('Titch') Somerfield
* Gilbert ('Gillie') Warne (1910-2000), son of Freddy Warne of Postbridge
* Thomas Redvers Webb (1901-1967), son of Jim and Kate Webb of Postbridge
* Henry (Harry) 'Silvertop' Warne (1878-1941), son of Solomon Warne
* Harry ('Ginger') Trude (1900-1979) with his son Alan
* Richard/Dick Perryman
* Ernest Webb, son of John Webb of Postbridge
* James/Jimmy Webb (1862-1951), tin dresser, of Postbridge
* William Webb (born 1902), son of John Webb of Postbridge.

At the front, the postmistress from Moretonhampstead is holding Panchaud's Alsatian dog Tor. The other two seated figures are friends or relatives of his. C. A. Panchaud himself is seated on the right. He was not

D. L. SMITH.

TORR TRUST, LTD.
GOLDEN DAGGER MINE,
POSTBRIDGE, DEVON.

well liked and had a reputation as a womaniser. Moreover he tended to have the same patronising attitude towards his Dartmoor workforce as he did towards native people working in colonial mines in west Africa. He had significant experience of tin mining in Nigeria and was keen to apply the same techniques to Dartmoor.[299]

He enjoyed travelling to London to visit women friends, and left Donald Smith to write regular reports on the mine. Donald had to send these to him in London via the Moretonhampstead postmistress. Panchaud copied them out in longhand and posted them back to Moretonhampstead, from where they were sent on to the Directors in London with the 'correct' Moretonhampstead postmark. This subterfuge worked well until one day Panchaud was spotted 'on the arm of a woman' in Chancery Lane by one of the directors who, not surprisingly, expected him to be on the mine. A telegram was immediately sent to the mine asking when Panchaud was last seen. With a motorcyclist waiting for a response, an honest answer was given.[300] This resulted in Panchaud being dismissed (probably in July 1927). Donald Smith was appointed as manager in his place, at the age of only twenty (Fig. 109). About every three months he had to travel to London for a company board meeting at Moorgate Station Chambers, dressing in a black morning coat, pinstripe trousers and bowler hat.[301]

One of the company bosses was Philip Bertie Spencer Stanhope (1868-1951) who lived not far away near Widecombe. He was said to be 'mining mad' and had actually been granted a one-year licence for Birch Tor & Vitifer and Golden Dagger as long ago as 1922.[302] He was from Cannon Hall, Barnsley in Yorkshire and had a BA degree in Mathematics, Physics, Chemistry and Classics from Oxford. In October 1895 he was admitted as an Associate Member of the Institution of Civil Engineers. In 1904 he married a Miss Scrimgeour of Natsworthy, Widecombe. He also had mining interests in British Columbia.[303]

He is likely to have been the author of a letter dated 2 October 1927, sent to Mr Thomas Davies, in which he suggested the introduction of some new methods:

'...I am certainly not satisfied with all the present methods of treating ground, and I am making improvements where possible...During August when the expert was here, I only carried on the work as Mr. Panchaud left it, but during September there has been certain alterations by which nearly all tramming except of heads from buddles and strips is done away with by moving the strips so that ground to be treated is close enough to be dug and shovelled direct on to the screen. The rotary screen or trommel which I have put in for feeding one buddle is probably the same idea as the expert has but is only of use where the ground to be treated is free from roots or slime of any kind and I cannot [think] of treating the latter unless by means of strips from which we used to loose [sic] a certain amount of fine tin, but owing to altering the construction of the strips this has mainly been prevented. The head of the strips is trammed to the buddles and fed by hand to the launder feeding the buddle. It is not a very simple thing to wash the head down to the buddle, and besides needing a great length of laundering it does not allow a head [?] pile of heads to accumulate under cover to keep the buddle running during wet weather. This is a minor consideration compared with other unnecessary labour that has been going on. The loss of tin in the rebuddling of concentrates is practically nothing, the tin-dresser is very keen on that, there being nothing th[r]own away that which could possibly contain workable tin. The Board have evidently mistaken my meaning with regard to the damming of the river in the cutting which I did to form a settling-pits as first mentioned in my letter of the 20th Aug. It is impossible for the settling-pits to wash as Reed and Smith state, they are nothing like full yet, and to pull down a wall built well to wash out what little sand that is in the pits would not be very profitable for us. The water bailiff has informed me that he is taking a sample of the water every week, and by that he showed me on Friday, it was practically clear.

The output of July left by Mr. Panchaud consisted of 21cwt. of undressed tin, and 3cwt. of seconds ready for market. The output for August consisted of 22cwt. of undressed tin of the same classes and proportions as that of July making 43cwt. and 3cwt. of seconds. This has given 22cwt. of 65% or over and 10cwt. of seconds about 50% tin, thus giving a loss of 14cwt contain[in]g fine tin, iron, black cockle, and heavy sand, which is far more than I expected. The fine tin will be recovered when there is sufficient quantity to make a buddle-full, and will go as seconds. The other loss is due to the fine iron sand and cockle, of which there was an extraordinary amount where we were working in July and August, and it is hard to distinguish this when with tin. The tin will be bagged and ready for despatching by Thursday. Do you not think it would be advisable to send only the 22cwt of best class tin and leave the seconds until we have a ton of this class?.'[304]

110. Petter Engine at Golden Dagger Mine. *P. J. Hill*

Fig. 110 shows the Petter engine when Donald Smith arrived. It was a 36hp semi-diesel twin cylinder oil engine. An air bottle and pump are visible on the left and a lubricating oil filter on the right. The belt on the right was used to drive an electric generator during very dry weather. The Petter engine replaced a more powerful 440v Producer Gas Engine which could produce about 200hp. The latter had special coal stored in the 'crib house'. Gas from burning the coal in a heating stove was mixed with air and powered the engine which had a flywheel about 8ft in diameter.[305]

111. View up valley to Dinah's House and abandoned stamps wheel, about 1927. *Donald Smith*

Fortunately Donald Smith himself took numerous photographs of the mine from at least 1927 – on a small Brownie camera and a Vest Pocket Kodak camera.[306] Fig. 111 looks up the valley towards the abandoned

stamps waterwheel. Fig. 112 is a

112. View up valley to Engine House about 1927. *Donald Smith*

'good view of the workings, engine house + dressing floors... On the right are three large trommel classifiers mounted on a steel pontoon which the Dartmoor Tin Mines Co experimented with before I came. They used the big gas engine to supply current to the motors driving suction pumps. The project was a failure but I made good use of much of the gear they left behind. Especially the 3½" steel pipes'.[307]

Fig. 113 shows the techniques of excavation of the tin-bearing ground either side of a tramway before being taken for washing. Fig. 114 is of four men from Plymouth. 'The second from left chased Panchaud up the tram

113. Tramway and ground being excavated about 1927. *Donald Smith*

114. Four men
with tram wagon
excavating ground
about 1927.
Donald Smith

lines threatening to cut his head off with a shovel. I had to give the chap
his cards and pay him off. After this Panchaud bought 'Tor' the dog for
some protection.'[308] He was 'a proper slave-driver, and also carried a pick
shaft with him, for defence.[309] The man on the right was called Tucker and
next to him is 'Big' Maclaughlin. The truck could be rotated and tipped
in any direction, and came from one of the 'Shiny Ore' mines in the
Lustleigh-Hennock area.[310]

Long sluices or stepped launders were introduced by Panchaud. In Fig.
115 a tailings pit is receiving the waste material. The side-tipping wagon
came from Vitifer. Two Plymouth men, who stayed in the Vitifer Bunk
House, are feeding material into the head of a sluice in Fig. 116. The
concentrate passes through a wire mesh to grade it. Donald commented
how useful the long-handled Cornish shovels were, with their hardened
steel tips. He could buy these for 10d each in Tavistock.[311]
Fig. 117 shows one of the flat screens feeding the launders.

The 'Engine House' with roofed dressing floors on its right, where the
final stages of tin processing took place, was sited about 150m below

115. Experimental sluices installed by Panchaud about 1927. *Donald Smith*

BOTTOM LEFT:
116. Two men at sluice head about 1927. *Donald Smith*

BOTTOM RIGHT:
117. Two men at sluice head with tram wagon about 1927. *Donald Smith*

118. Engine House etc about 1927. *Donald Smith*

Dinah's House, at SX 68557990. Fig. 118 shows the scene from the west before Donald Smith developed the equipment. The first concrete round buddles installed by Panchaud can be seen – these were made by a firm from Moretonhampstead. Also seen is the shelter for the Wilfley and Borden concentration (shaking) tables. Donald had the latter 'running for Flewin but Panchaud did not use them.' Donald recalled that the pipe in the foreground froze and burst one evening as he passed underneath – 'It was like a cannon shot!'[312]

Fig. 119 shows one of the first 'trommels' devised by Donald. No crushing was done, but six spikes inside the revolving trommels broke up

119. Original trommel about 1927. *Donald Smith*

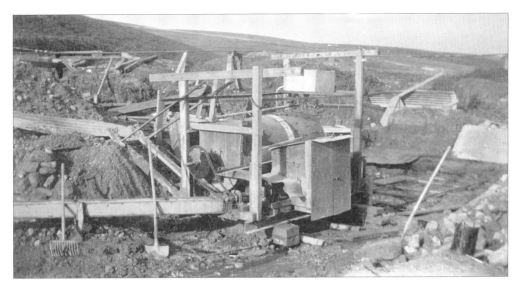

material, sometimes quite clayey, dug out of the old stream bed. A steel cylinder about 2ft in diameter contained three concentric meshes of 1-inch, $\frac{1}{4}$-inch and $\frac{1}{16}$-inch. This was 'the first unit driven by a 3HP electric motor which used to be used to drive the concentration tables. This unit fed directly into the buddle.'[313] Further development is shown in Fig. 120 with a small conveyor belt taking away waste. Note the multi-pronged stone fork as used by roadmen at the time. In Fig. 121 the conveyor belt is being fitted to the powered trommel. Redvers Webb holds the barrow; Bill Webb is at the rear.

120. Developed trommel about 1927. *Donald Smith*

121. Developed trommel with Engine House in background about 1927. *Donald Smith*

122. View over round buddles to Engine House about 1927. *Donald Smith*

Fig. 122 looks over buddles towards the Engine House. The tailings race around the buddle allowed quicker cleaning as 'the tailings washed straight to the settling pits'.[314] A round buddle used for 'heads', sited close to the Engine House, is seen in Fig. 123, looking westwards. The path on the opposite hill was used by miners going to and from Postbridge.

Redvers Webb is seen in Fig. 124 cleaning out a buddle just below the upper workings near the Engine House. 'We made all our

123. Round buddle etc by Engine House about 1927. *Donald Smith*

124. Redvers Webb and round buddle by workings near Engine House about 1927. *Donald Smith*

own barrows. One special big barrow we made as a bit of a joke for Fred Warne and he loaded it with 12 sacks of cement and pushed it from Dinah's cottage to the engine house! We made all our water wheels too. Five waterwheels & two raff wheels altogether'.[315]

There were several more buddles at the 'middle' workings, about 200m downstream, on the right (west) bank at SX 685797 (Fig. 125).

125. Buddles etc at 'middle' workings about 1927. *Donald Smith*

126. Waterwheel
and buddles at
'middle' workings
about 1927.
Donald Smith

Fig. 126 shows buddles and a waterwheel at the middle workings. In Fig.
127 Redvers Webb is feeding one of the buddles of the middle workings.
The 'sweeps' and the launder feeding over the centre cone are clearly
visible, as is the concentrate building up. Harry Warne is in Fig. 128
working in a 'heads' buddle.

One innovation of Donald Smith's was to install a turbine at the
Engine House. Fig. 129 shows concrete being mixed outside the Engine

127. Redvers Webb feeding round buddle in 'middle' workings about 1927. *Donald Smith*

128. Harry Warne at 'middle' workings about 1927. *Donald Smith*

129. Mixing concrete for turbine pipeline about 1927. *Donald Smith*

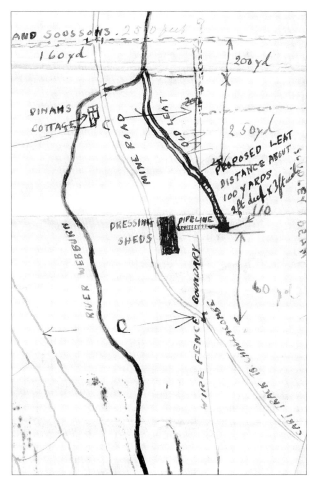

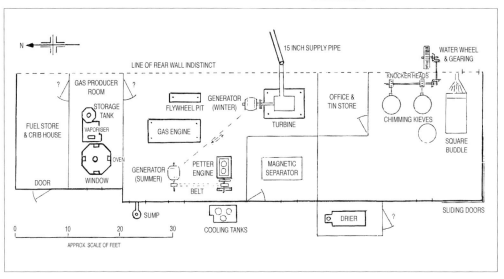

130. Plan of pipeline route 9 November 1927

House, as part of the works for the new leat and pipe to the turbine. 25 tons of concrete were used in one day. The men were happy to work on a Sunday without any 'double time' for pay.[316] Fig. 130 is a plan of the pipeline route dated 9 November 1927. It appears that there had been an earlier turbine on the mine, seemingly immediately upstream of Dinah's House. Correspondence in December 1920 and January 1921 reveals that a turbine and a length of iron pipe was sold from the mine, either to W. H. Hosking of Newton Abbot or to Mr Perryman of Yeo Mills, Chagford.[317]

Based on Donald Smith's detailed descriptions, and surviving concrete footings, a plan of the Engine House was prepared by Peter Richardson (Fig. 131).[318]

131. Plan of Engine House by P. H. G. Richardson.

The only known view inside the dressing floors is given in Fig. 132. C. A. Panchaud is on the left, Donald Smith in the centre, and tin dresser Jim Webb on the right. James (Jim/Jimmy) Webb (1862-1951) was renowned as a tin dresser. He had long associations with both Vitifer and Golden Dagger, but had also been a tin dresser at Wheal Friendship, Mary Tavy[319] better known for its copper and arsenic production. He made a strange whistling noise through his nose, thought to have been due to working with arsenic. He was the son of Tom Webb. He married Kate Coaker, the sister of John James Coaker at Princetown on 25 October 1899.[320] In 1901 they were living at Cape Horn (Fig. 74). He worked in gold mines, probably in both India and South Africa, and made sufficient money to build himself a house at Tor View, Postbridge in 1907 (Fig. 133) which still exists (though threatened with demolition). Jack Hamlyn recalled how he pegged out a route from there across the moor to Golden Dagger to define a path before it became well used.[321]

132.
C.A. Panchaud, Donald Smith and Jim Webb inside Engine House about 1927.
Photographer not known

119

133. Tor View,
Postbridge, built
by Jim Webb
1907. *Photographer
not known*

As tin dresser at Golden Dagger, Jim Webb was the highest paid
workman on £2 5s per week. Freddy Warne received £2 2s, while the
rest of the men got £2 (or 10d per hour), Donald Smith received £3 and
Panchaud £6. When Donald took over as manager his, Jimmy Webb's
and Freddy Warne's rates were increased by 5s, and Redvers Webb
received £2 2s.[322]

The large tub in front of the men is a chimming kieve. It has been
moved for the purpose of the photograph to show how Jim Webb would
use his packing bar. The largest item of equipment is a square buddle, and
in the foreground a vanning shovel rests on the top of a small kieve which
rests on a floor (chimming floor) at a slightly lower level, so that water
could quickly drain away when kieves were emptied. Two piles of tin
concentrate can be seen beside the head of the square buddle which is
supplied with water by the vertical pipe leading from a wooden launder.
Just visible, propped against the galvanised side wall, is a heather brush
which would have been used in the square buddle by the tin dresser.

There was also a magnetic separator in the shed. Once the 'heads' had
passed through the square buddle, they were dried in a steel trough about
8ft x 3ft, heated by a flue and fire fuelled with wood. They were then fed
onto a belt made of canvas with a rubber surface, about 18 inches wide and
8ft long and, passing over two wheels each 2ft in diameter, it was moved
forward very slowly. This belt cost £15. A second belt, which was only $^1/_{16}$"
thick, passed at right angles to the other. Huge and powerful magnets
would be positioned above and below the belts. The height of the magnet
could be adjusted depending on whether the tin was coarse or fine – it had
to be watched very carefully. As the tin, mixed with specular haematite
(which was not highly magnetic), passed between the magnets, the iron was
attracted onto the underside of one of the belts. Once beyond the influence
of the magnets, the iron would drop off the belt. The tin fell into a box at

134. Buddles at lower workings under construction, with Challacombe Down in background about 1928. *Donald Smith*

the end. The magnetic flux was very intense – a spanner a yard away would be attracted to it. The air around the separator would be filled with a fine bluish iron dust. Only Donald Smith and Redvers Webb worked here.[323]

From here the concentrate was taken to the chimming kieve. The concentrate was kept in suspension by stirring with a special paddle known as a 'chimming shovel'. It was then 'packed' by hand with a bar, though Donald later installed a system of mechanical packing powered by a waterwheel. It took two men to tip up the kieve and pour the water off it, until it was vertically on edge. The top surface would then be skimmed off and the richness of the deposit would be judged by its colour. Concentrate might be put through a kieve two or three times.[324]

The lower workings, developed from about 1928 onwards, were in the bottom reaches of the Redwater valley where it widens out between Soussons and Challacombe, at SX 689791. Fig. 134 shows round buddles under construction here with Challacombe Down in the background, and Fig. 135 is of the same site, but looking towards Soussons. The

135. Waterwheel and buddles under construction at lower workings, with view towards Soussons about 1928. *Donald Smith*

136. Round buddle in lower workings about 1928.
Donald Smith

waterwheel was of cast iron and had previously been used at the upper workings near the Engine House. Donald Smith and his workforce had 'plenty of good sand and Belgian cement was £12 for a 10 ton load'. Initially this came in 2cwt sacks but later in paper bags holding 1cwt.[325] One of the buddles was smaller than the others, and was used for treating heads before being carted to the dressing floors. Fig. 136 is of a buddle in the lower workings.

Of particular interest are the moveable trommel units devised by Donald Smith for the lower workings. They incorporated wooden buddles about 12-15ft in diameter. Each unit cost £50-£60. In 1929 'prospects were so good' as it was thought that the tin price would be 'rationalised' at £300 per ton. Donald proposed working them ten abreast up the valley but this was considered too extravagant by most of the directors. Fig. 137 shows the first move up the valley, with Challacombe Down behind, using pipes as rollers on rails which could be taken up and placed ahead, the space behind being filled with waste stone and tailings. 'It was planned to use several of these units side by side right up the valley. They were found to be the most effective method of working' at the time of closure in

122

1930.[326] Fig.138 is another view of the units, looking towards Soussons Farm. Water for washing and for driving waterwheels was brought by pipe from further up the valley.

Once the lower workings and buddles had been developed, concentrates could be produced that were good enough to be taken direct to the dressing floors and worked on the square buddles. 'We transferred

137. Moveable units + trommel, with Challacombe Down behind about 1928. *Donald Smith*

138. Moveable units + trommel, with view to Soussons Farm about 1928. *Donald Smith*

139. Horse and
cart with Jim and
Redvers Webb
about 1928.
Donald Smith

these by using a horse and cart hired from Jack Withycombe [of Soussons
Farm] and we were able to tip right onto the dressing floor' (Fig. 139).
Jim Webb and his son Redvers are in the photograph.[327]

The lorry in Fig. 140 is a Willy's Overland Crossley with number plate
DR 5531[328] and belonged to Frank and Jack Petherick of Princetown. It
transported bags of tin to Princetown Station. The bags were 8in in
diameter x 2ft 6in high and would hold 3cwt of tin. Smaller bags,
supplied by the Penryn Metal Co. were used later, holding 1cwt.[329] Harry
Warne, Tommy Petherick and Jim Webb are on the lorry, with Redvers
Webb and Frank Williams (1908-1993) on the right.[330] Frank (Francis
Edmund Curfew) Williams was born into a large family (eighteen in total)
at Thurso on 20 March 1908. His paternal grandfather moved from
Peterhead prison to Dartmoor to be a Principal Warder. Frank lived at
Bellever and worked for a time at Runnage Farm, Postbridge. In 1926 he

140. Petherick
lorry about 1928.
Donald Smith

124

went to work at Golden Dagger Mine, riding his pushbike via Dury and Pizwell. He much admired Donald Smith and stayed there for about six months, and then went to work on the roads for Mark Loram. He died on 9 January 1993 and is buried at Doddiscombsleigh.[331]

Fig. 141 shows Donald Smith looking very proud having built his first waterwheel, and Fig. 142 shows him on his motorcycle. For most of his time at Golden Dagger he lodged at Soussons Farm (Fig. 143) with the Withycombe family. He was known as 'Longboy' by the workforce. He himself occasionally had accidents – he once slipped off a plank in the ice at the lower workings and caught a severe blow on his chest which badly bruised his ribs. He had a very painful journey to attend a board meeting in London where he saw his doctor who strapped him up. On another occasion an iron bar struck him across the nose when he was working in the turbine pit.[332]

141. Donald Smith and his first waterwheel about 1927.
Photographer not known

142. Donald Smith on his motorcycle about 1927.
Photographer not known

143. Soussons Farm about 1927. *Donald Smith*

Fig. 144 is a fine picture of Harry Warne in a working context on the mine. His demon was drink and he spent much of his wages in the Warren House Inn,[333] which made life very difficult for his wife Polly and daughter Beatie. Donald Smith would sometimes take £1 out of Harry Warne's wages in order to ensure that they had enough food. Beatie, when aged about twelve, once had to go up to the Warren Inn at midnight with her mother, to collect her father.[334] In the 1920s the landlord at the Warren House Inn was William ('Billy Buck') Stephens who had himself worked as a carpenter at Vitifer (Fig. 145). Tragically he committed suicide in the pub, by shooting himself, in March 1929. His wife Mary and daughter Selina (Lena) (Fig. 146) carried on for a short while, until Arthur Hurn took over in 1930.[335]

144. Harry Warne with shovel about 1927. *Photographer not known, ex Sinclair*

BOTTOM LEFT:
145. William Stephens, landlord of the Warren House Inn 1921-1929. *John Weston*

BOTTOM RIGHT:
146. Mary Stephens, landlady of the Warren House Inn 1929-1930, with her daughter Selina (Lena). *John Weston*

Ernest Webb by a buddle is in Fig. 147, and Jim Webb with his son
Redvers are in Fig. 148. Donald Smith commented, 'Both fine characters'.[336]

The workforce from the Plymouth Labour Exchange were of more
mixed calibre. Four are seen in Fig. 149. The tallest was called
Maclaughlin and was 'a very good worker'.[337] He lived with his wife and
baby in the old Golden Dagger Dry, which Beatie Brook (née Warne)
remembered had three rooms, none of which connected to another, so that
when she lived there as a child, and needed to go to bed, she had to step
outside and re-enter the building. There was a hen-house at one end, and
an outside toilet.[338]

148. Redvers and
Jim Webb about
1927. *Donald Smith*

127

149. Four workmen about 1927. *Donald Smith*

A good group of nine workers posed near the old stamps wheel is shown in Fig. 150. Harry Warne is in the centre of the front row. Ten men outside the dressing floors shed are in Fig. 151. Jim Webb is on the left. Donald Smith is in the centre of the back row, with managerial tie. Harry Warne kneels on the left. Redvers Webb stands third from left, Ernest Webb stands second from right, and Maclaughlin is on the extreme right. The others are unidentified men from Plymouth. Fig. 152 shows haircutting in progress.

150. Group of miners near old stamps wheel about 1927. *Photographer not known, ex Sinclair*

151. Group outside
Engine House
about 1927.
P. Sinclair

152. Haircutting
about 1927, Ernest
Webb and Jock
Shaw. *Donald Smith*

Fig. 153 is interesting as it is a reminder of the core energy source for these mines. A leat was taken off the Dart and Teign rivers some seven miles (11 km) into the moor. The men are high up the East Dart River, close to the headweir of one branch of the mine leat which they have been cleaning out, as well as repairing breaks in its bank. From left to right are Ernest Webb, Alex (Jock) Shaw, Freddy Warne and his dog Vick, Bill Webb, Gilbert Warne (with binoculars), and Jim Warne (no close relation). Gilbert Warne (1910-2000) was Freddy's son.

153. Group on moor by leat headweir about 1927. *Donald Smith*

He first went to work at Golden Dagger in 1924, earning 7s 6d per week. He once managed to drive a newly-sharpened pick into the instep of his foot, and Donald Smith had great difficulty in removing the impacted leather boot. Donald drove him to Moretonhampstead hospital on his motorbike[339]

Alex 'Jock' Shaw was a Scotsman who came to work at Bellever Farm when Galloway cattle were introduced for the first time. Donald Smith remembered him as 'a good worker, clever with mechanical gear'.[340] 'Jock' Shaw encouraged his 13-year-old brother-in-law Ken 'Lofty' Williams, also living at Bellever, to play truant from Postbridge school to earn 'a few bob' at Golden Dagger Mine. This he did for several months until the school attendance officer caught up with him. One of his odd jobs on the mine was to fetch bottles of beer for the men from the Warren House Inn in a sack, when the 'boss' was away.[341]

Despite Donald Smith's best efforts he couldn't compete against a falling price of tin. By 1930 it was only £120 per ton, compared to £315 when he arrived at the mine in 1925, and the mine closed on 12 November 1930.[342]. Donald spent about four days in Cornwall trying, unsuccessfully, to sell the Petter engine to quarries, etc. Eventually it was sold elsewhere for about £150.[343] Donald Smith went on to have a successful teaching career, mostly in Brighton.

An inventory and valuation was made in February 1931 of materials on the mine belonging to Torr Trust Ltd. Valued at less than £25, they seem to have been bought by Philip Stanhope:[344]

2 Oak Chimming Kieves 2£ each	£4.0.0
3 universal tip wagons, set of points, 68 rails, 118 iron sleepers – box of dogs – 1 b? wide wheel	£15.0.0
3 Vanning Shovels	5.0
1 Iron Wheelbarrow for floors	10.0
4 [?] separator iron bolts	10.0
100 Tin Bags	£ 2.0.0
20 1½" Plumber Blocks	1.0.0
50ft Shafting with 2 bearings	10.0
4 Screens (2 round 2 oblong)	8.0
	£24.18.0

[the correct sum is £24.3.0]

In June 1932 the mine house was advertised to be let, and 'suitable for holiday party'. It was described as having '3 bedrooms, large sitting-room, 2 partly-furnished rooms; water laid on; garage, stabling, and barn'.[345]

Stanhope had established an informal partnership with Keith Fox of Natsworthy in 1931, and a bizarre meeting was held at Dinah's House in the mid-1930s over a lunch of 'bully beef and red wine', between them and Duchy officials to discuss the future of the mine.[346]

By the late summer of 1934 Harry Vernon Olver was living in Dinah's House and probably actively working tin on a small scale. Inventories were prepared in August and September 1934 of furniture and fittings at 'Golden Dagger Mine House' i.e. Dinah's House, all apparently belonging to Philip Stanhope.

Against the listing of three old iron bedsteads, one large trestle table, one large measure or rule, 2 of 8 large forks, 2 of 8 tablespoons and 2 of 10 dessertspoons is a handwritten note 'on loan to Mr Olver'.[347]

The handwritten inventory of 16 September 1934 itemises all furniture and fittings belonging to Mr P. Stanhope at Golden Dagger Mine House (Postbridge) and left in charge of Mr Vernon Olver. [348] The artefacts provide unique insight into domestic life at Golden Dagger at this time:

2 Wood Camp Bedsteads

5 Blankets

1 Red Indian Blanket

2 Rugs

2 Pillows

4 Sheets

2 Pillow Cases

2 Folding Camp Tables

1 small occasional Table

1 Writing Table without top

1 Washstand

1 Basket Chair

1 small armchair (taken by Mr.S. 21/8/34)

2 Bedroom Chairs cane seats

1 do stuff seat

1 Mahogany Dining Table

1 Kitchen Table

3 Wood Forms

1 Stool. Upholsrered

2 china water Ewers, 1 broken

1 Enamelled Tin Ewer

3 Wash Basins 1 cracked (1 ewer broken and no use)

3 Soap Dishes

1 Tooth Brush Dish

2 Iron Coal Scuttles

1 small fire Shovel

2 Buckets

1 Perfection 3 burner oil Stove with oven

1 single oil Stove without reservoir

1 small single oil Stove

1 small metal oil Lamp broken

2 lined serge Curtains

2 unlined ditto

I Green Table Cloth

1 large Iron Saucepan

1 Iron Kettle

1 Aluminium Egg Saucepan no lid

2 Frying Pans

1 Scrubbing Brush

3 Iron Bedsteads

1 large Spanner

1 Cold Chisel

1 large American Saw

1 Pickaxe

1 Hammer

1 Screw Hammer

1 Horse Cloth

1 large Trestle Table

1 Glass Coffee Maker

1 Breakfast Cup & Saucer

1 do no handle

2 Tea Cups

1 Milk Jug cracked

1 small Jug

2 Tea Pots

1 Aluminium Coffee Pot

1 Sugar Jar

5 Dinner Plates

3 Dessert Plates

2 Tea Plates

3 Fruit Dishes

3 Vegatable [sic] Dishes 1 chipped

1 large Casserole

5 Chambers

6 large Forks

5 small Forks

2 Stainless Steel Knives

5 large Knives

6 small do

6 Table Spoons

8 Dessert Spoons

2 Tea Spoons

1 Tin opener

1 Hand Bowl

1 Funnel

1 large Measure or Rule

4 Paint & Varied Brushes

2 Wheelbarrows

1 Wood Stand for wall with shelf

2 Wardrobes

1 Mahogany Table Top

1 Fire Iron

1 Pair Fire Tongs

2 Padded Wicker Baskets

1 Coppered Tray

I Marble Slab

1 large T square mahogany

1 aluminium Dish Cover

Pictures

1 Glass Measure

1 Candlestick enamelled

1 Tumbler

1 fruit Glass

Harry Vernon Olver (1892-1943) (Fig. 154) was from Bodmin, and had had a distinguished career in the First World War, being awarded the

154. Dressing plant set up by H. V. Olver, 26 September 1937. *P. H. G. Richardson*

Military Medal.[349] By 1929 he was living at Wheal Maria Cottages[350] at Devon Great Consols, and may well have been actively involved in the mine there.

Between June and November 1935 Harry Olver and Stanhope acquired various, generally unsatisfactory, assays of samples of tin ground from Bristol, London and Vancouver.[351] In March 1936, Olver obtained a quotation for six steel plates each 6ft x 2ft 6in x $1/8$ in. thick, perforated with one-inch or half-inch holes from J & F Pool, Ltd of Hayle, Cornwall. These were delivered to the mine in early May 1936 and cost £7 5s.[352] An invoice survives from April 1936 when Olver ordered timber from Jewsons of Plymouth, totalling £7 10s 2d.[353]

Olver was still at Golden Dagger in 1937 when visited by Peter Richardson[354] and a photograph of some of his equipment is shown in Fig. 154.

David Hurn (born 1917), the son of Arthur Hurn who took over as publican at the Warren House Inn in 1930, knew Olver as 'Snag' because he was always hitting problems.[355] Bill Withycombe, the local postman, remembered him as 'a very nice fellow' who 'worked hard there to try to make it go'.[356]

Although Stanhope acquired further leases from the Duchy of Cornwall in 1938 to work Golden Dagger and alluvial ground to the south,[357] and significant testing was carried out by H. Douglas Allen,[358] on 8 May 1939 he wrote to Donald Smith:[359]

'At last I think the Golden Dagger Mine is finished.

Last year it looked very promising. I gave an option to a Mr Roberts who passed it on to a Mr Salt a London financier who expended over £1000 in sinking shafts and bores under the management of a Mr Allen stated to be the leading tin expert in England [and] a member of the Mining Inst. He got down 35 feet in tin all the way and was very pleased with assays etc. A large company was formed with £50,000 capital and then came the crisis and the whole thing shut up with a bang.

Mr Salt has since been trying to start a new concern and persuaded [me] to renew my licences but lately put me off, put me off finally putting off even taking up an option at all till I chucked the whole business and got a release from the Duchy who were very civil indeed over the matter. But the very next day sold the whole property to the Forestry Commissions.

Now Mr Salt is abusing me for throwing up the finest money making concern in the Kingdom and Mr Allen is abroad reporting on a tin concern in Nigeria and will be angry and sick when he returns.

So far as I am concerned I have still to try and get the Trust [?] manager a job. He is an expert electrician though he has no papers of examination etc – and I have to sell or remove the plant in a reasonable time.

And I want your opinion on the idea of setting up an electrical plant for my house with part of the plant – especially the pipes.

There are a large quantity of 3 inch pipes (you probably remember them) and a small lot of 7 inch pipes.

With the 3 inch pipes I can bring the water from the stream 550 feet with a fall of 2 feet fast [?] enough to make a good [sic] flow here. I can make a large tank say 1000 gallons from which I can get a fall of 76 feet + 4 feet depth of tank with a fall of 1 foot in 3 feet.

This seems to me a [sic] ideal for a Pelton Wheel – but I do not know enough of the requirements for electrical plant to know what can be done. Could you give me any help or even come and pay me a visit at Whitsuntide to see for yourself?'

Then came the Second World War. Harry Olver signed up and went to France with the British Expeditionary Force. He was taken prisoner when a Captain in the Duke of Cornwall's Light Infantry and died on 25 August 1943 in a hospital at Schmorkau near Dresden. A fine portrait of him survives (Fig. 155).[360]

Irene Bailey (née French in 1915) lived with her parents at Soussons Farm and recalled that Stanhope installed a couple called Mr & Mrs Thicknesse at Dinah's House after Olver. They had previously managed a gunshop in London but had fallen on hard times.[361] A report on Birch Tor,

155.
Harry Vernon
Olver.

Vitifer and Golden Dagger Mines dated 21 February 1942 was made by Stevenson Buchan of HM Geological Survey. He concluded that the 'mines are not recommended as potential quick producers of tin'.[362]

The last occupants of Dinah's House were Harry and Polly Warne. On 13 November 1942 Harry, who suffered from epilepsy, had a fall onto the kitchen fire, and severely burnt his left hand. He died in hospital six weeks later, on 28 December, aged sixty-four.[363]

156. Abandoned
stamps waterwheel,
26 September
1937. *P. H. G.
Richardson*

157. Remains of
wooden buddle, 26
September 1937.
P. H. G. Richardson

Golden Dagger Mine — back to the land

The abandoned stamps wheel, still with stamps attached, but no longer within a shed, were photographed by Peter Richardson on 26 September 1937 (Fig. 156). On the same day he photographed the remains of a wooden buddle (Fig. 157), probably once attached to a moveable trommel unit.

A view up the Redwater valley from Soussons Down in the mid-1930s (Fig. 158) gives a good impression of abandoned mine wheels and buildings in the landscape before the Second World War.

During the Second World War the mine buildings were demolished 'by soldiers who used the stones for road building'.[364]

On a visit to Golden Dagger Mine on 14 April 1971, I recorded the

158. View up Redwater valley about 1935. *Photographer not known, ex Claude Warren*

159. Dinah's House from west 14 April 1971. *T. Greeves*

160. Round buddles ('middle' workings) on right (west) bank of Redwater valley, SX 68557968, 5 May 1974. *T. Greeves*

ruins of Dinah's House (Fig. 159). Today there is still a substantial ruin there, partly consolidated by Dartmoor National Park Authority. Some of the buddles of Donald Smith's 'middle' workings at SX 68557968 are shown in Fig. 160, as they appeared in May 1974, and the pipe leading to the turbine at the Engine House still survives (Fig. 161).

Much of the area was planted with coniferous trees in the late 1940s. Some features have since been cleared of trees, but naturally regenerating scrub obscures much, and the area is constantly changing in appearance. Many other features gently reach a state of stable archaeological decay. However, thanks to the legacy of contemporary photographs and oral testimony, the long and fascinating human story of mining in this valley since about 1900 can still be brought to life, and the miners 'called home'.

161. Turbine pipe at Engine House, May 2000.
Scale: 1m. *T. Greeves*

References

1. Anon, 2014

2. Thorndycraft et al, 2004

3. Meharg et al, 2012

4. Greeves, 1981

5. Blake, 1915

6. Greeves, 2015, 26-7

7. Greeves, 1986, 23

8. cf. Newman, 2002, 32

9. Broughton, 1968-9, 36-38

10. North Bovey Census 1851

11. Greeves & Stanbrook, 2012, 19

12. Broughton, 1968-9, 38

13. Broughton, 1968-9, 27

14. Broughton, 1968-9, 37

15. Oral inf. Ernest Worth 18.3.1970

16. Greeves, 1980; 2002

17. Newman, 2002, 41-3

18. Greeves, 2012; oral inf. Annie Sleep 25.9.1969

19. The 'missing' ones are numbers 11940, 11945, 11946, 11948, 11951, 11957, 11958, 11959. Apart from 11940 which is probably of Golden Dagger, the others (if published) are likely to be of Vitifer.

20. Greeves, 1986, 23

21. Letter from William Grose 1.12.1974

22. Letter from William Grose 6.11.1977

23. Rowe, 1848, 266

24. Greeves, 1981; 1986, 4

25. Greeves, 1986, 4; Newman, 1996

26. Greeves, 1986, 4

27. Macdonald, n.d.

28. Letter from William Grose 11.12.1977

29. Du(chy) Co(rnwall) London, Mineral Grants Vol.1; Howard, 1993

30. Greeves, 1986, 6

31. Brown, 1999, Vol.25, 14

32. Letter from William Grose 19.3.1976

33. *London & West Country Chamber of Mines, Records 1904-1907*, p.259

34. Letter from William Grose, rec'd September 1977

35. Idem

36. Letter from William Grose 19.3.1976

37. Notebook, conversation with William Grose 1.8.1981; for more detail on the Grose family see Wilson, 2015

38. Greeves, 1986, 4

39. Notebook 1.8.1981

40. DuCo London, Mineral Grants Vol.1

41. Letter from William Grose, rec'd November 1976

42. Letter from William Grose, rec'd September 1977

43. Letter from William Grose, rec'd November 1976

44. Oral inf. A.J.Grose, 12.9.1974

45. Letter from William Grose, rec'd November 1976

46. Letter from William Grose, rec'd September 1977

47. Oral inf. William Grose, tape 3.8.1981

48. Notebook, conversation with William Grose 1.8.1981

49   Oral inf. William Grose, tape 3.8.81

50   Oral inf. William Grose, tape 3.8.1981

51   Idem

52   Letter from William Grose 19.3.1976; Notebook, conversation with Gertrude Prew 3.10.1984

53   Oral inf. William Grose, tape 3.8.1981

54   Notebook, conversation with Gertrude Prew 9.7.1977

55   Letter from William Grose 11.12.1977

56   Letter from William Grose 19.3.1976; Census 1901

57   Letter from Frank Chudley 25.10.1987

58   Falcon, 1903

59   Letter from William Grose 11.12.1977

60   Oral inf. William Grose, tape 3.8.1981

61   Notebook 15.8.1992

62   Copy Indenture signed G. Heaton, in possn TG

63   Letter from William Grose, rec'd November 1976

64   Notebook, conversation with William Grose 1.8.1981

65   Letter from William Grose, rec'd November 1976; letter from William Grose 6.11.1977

66   Letter from William Grose, rec'd November 1976

67   Greeves, 1986, 4

68   Oral inf. William Grose, tape 3.8.1981

69   Greeves, 1985; Greeves, 1986, 18

70   Letter from Lilian Jones 20.9.1984

71   Oral inf. William Grose, tape 3.8.1981

72   Richardson, 1992, 35

73   Letter from William Grose, rec'd November 1976

74   Letter from William Grose 26.2.1982

75   Notebook, conversation with William Grose 1.8.1981

76   Oral inf. William Grose, tape October 1986

77   Greeves, 1986,7

78   Notebook, conversation with M. Spiller 16.12.1980

79   Notebook, conversation with William Grose 1.8.1981

80   Idem

81   Letter from William Grose 28.9.1978

82   Notebook, conversation with William Grose 1.8.1981

83   Oral inf. William Grose, tape 3.8.1981

84   *Western Morning News* 10.1.1908, inf. C J Kelland

85   Notebook, conversation with William Grose 2.8.1981

86   Letter from William Grose 28.9.1978

87   Letter from William Grose 3.11.1980

88   Oral inf. William Grose, tape 3.8.1981

89   Letter from William Grose, rec'd September 1977

90   Idem

91   Letters from William Grose 10.2.1978; 28.9.1978

92   Oral inf. William Grose, tape 3.8.1981

93   Letter from William Grose 10.2.1978; oral inf. William Grose, tape 3.8.1981; cf. oral inf. Frank Warne, who worked at Vitifer Mine from 1914, who said that the Tin Chest there had 'three or four padlocks on it', tape 30.10.73.

94   Notebook, conversation with William Grose 1.8.1981

95   Letter from William Grose, rec'd September 1977; Notebook, conversation with William Grose 2.8.1981

96   Oral inf. William Grose, tape 3.8.1981

97 *Tavistock Gazette* 8 Nov 1889 – inf. C J Kelland

98 Wikipedia

99 Letter from William Grose, rec'd September 1977

100 Oral inf. William Grose, tape 3.8.1981; Greeves, 1992, 15

101 Pryce, 1778, 329

102 Oral inf. William Grose, tape 3.8.1981; Greeves, 2010

103 Letter from William Grose, rec'd September 1977

104 Letter from William Grose, rec'd November 1976

105 Oral inf. William Grose, tape 3.8.1981

106 Oral inf. William Grose, tape October 1986

107 Oral inf. William Grose, tape 3.8.1981

108 Cornwall Record Office/TL 104/31

109 Oral inf. William Grose, tape 3.8.1981

110 Idem

111 Letter from William Grose, rec'd September 1977

112 Oral inf. William Grose, tape 3.8.1981

113 Idem

114 Letter from William Grose 10.2.1978

115 Greeves, 1986, 12; Notebook 10.5.1977; 9.7.1977

116 Letter from William Grose, rec'd February 1978

117 Oral inf. William Grose, tape 3.8.1981

118 Idem

119 Oral inf. William Grose, tape October 1986

120 Notebook, conversation with William Grose 1.8.1981

121 Notebook, conversation with William Grose 15.10.1986

122 Letter from William Grose 31.5.1981

123 Oral inf. William Grose, tape 3.8.1981

124 Oral inf. William Grose, tape 3.8.1981

125 Notebook, conversation with Bill Warren 6.7.1972

126 Greeves, 2011

127 Notebook, conversation with Emily Coaker 13.12.1979

128 Notebook, conversation with Bill Warren 6.7.1972

129 Notebook, conversation with Fernley Warne (Postbridge) 11.9.1970

130 Greeves, 1986, 13

131 Notebook, conversation with Robert Savery 12.1.2012. He had been told the story by Harry Norrish of Combestone Farm

132 Oral inf. William Grose, tape 3.8.1981

133 Notebook, conversations with Bill Warren 6.7.1972 and 31.8.1972

134 Notebook, conversation with Emily Coaker 13.12.1979

135 Oral inf. Sidney French, tape 4.2.1974

136 Notebook, conversation with Fernley Warne 11.9.1970

137 Notebook, conversation with Marjorie Cooper 1.8.76

138 Oral inf. Annie Sleep, tape 10.8.1970

139 Letter from William Grose, rec'd November 1976

140 Oral inf. William Grose, tape 3.8.1981

141 Idem

142 Oral inf. William Grose, tape October 1986

143 Letter from William Grose 19.3.1976

144 Letter from William Grose 13.7.1980

145 Greeves, 1986, 12; for appreciations of William Grose see Greeves, 1995; 2000a.

146 *The London & West Country Chamber of Mines, Records 1904-1907*, pp 138, 208, 211, 212

146 Idem, p.176

148 Idem, pp 235-6

149 Cornwall Record Office X955/7, transcript provided by C J Kelland

150 *The London & West Country Chamber of Mines, Records 1904-1907*, p.236

151 Greeves, 1986, 12

152 *The London & West Country Chamber of Mines, Records 1904-1907*, p.236

153 Greeves, 1986, 10

154 Oral inf. Annie Sleep, tape 10.8.1970; notebook, conversation with Bill Warren 31.8.1972; conversation with Annie Sleep 9.3.1982

155 Oral inf. Annie Sleep, tape 10.8.1970

156 Oral inf. Frank Warne, tape 30.10.1973

157 Notebook, conversation with Charles & Joan French 11.12.1990

158 Letter from William Grose, rec'd November 1976

159 Reid *et al*, 1912, 74

160 Greeves, 1986, 6

161 Richardson, 1992, 34; Greeves, 2011e

162 Notebook, conversation with Mrs Chaffe 25.2.1983

163 Notebook, conversation with Kenneth Williams, 19.6.1986

164 Notebook, conversations with George Robertson Owen, 2.2.2005 and 4.2.2005

165 Greeves, 1986, 21

166 Greeves, 1986, 21, 23; Broughton, 1971, 15

167 Letter written by Moses Bawden 21 January 1903(?) and published in local newspaper, in possn Sylvia Sayer.

168 Notebook, conversation with Mrs Bents 30.10.1973

169 Notebook, conversation with Beatie Brook 10.7.1977 and Mrs Chaffe 25.2.1983

170 Notebook, conversation with Tom Hill 29.10.1978

171 Greeves, 1986, 26

172 Notebook, conversation with Donald Smith 26.5.1983

173 Greeves, 1986, 41; Burt *et al*, 1984, 16

174 Notebook, conversation with Donald Smith 26.5.1983

175 Oral inf. Donald Smith, tape 16.8.1984 [check]

176 Greeves, 1986,26

177 Notebook, conversation with Mrs Chaffe 25.2.1983; Greeves, 1986, 26

178 According to Robert Burnard in notes written by him in the late nineteenth century opposite Ordnance Survey Sheet 99NE (in possn Sylvia Sayer) he recorded that 'the date on the large bell outside the Count house is 1807'

179 Greeves, 1986, 26

180 Kits House Gully was marked by Robert Burnard in the late nineteenth century on Ordnance Survey Sheet 99 NE (in possn Sylvia Sayer)

181 DuCo London, Mineral Grants Vol.1; Greeves, 1986, 27

182 Greeves, 1986, 28

183 Notebook, conversation with Gilbert Warne 4.10.1983

184 Letter from A J Gale 28.4.01

185 Notebook, conversation with Ethel White 30.10.73 and Sidney French 25.4.74

186 Letter from Brenda Short 20.10.85

187 Notebook, conversation with Gilbert Warne 5.10.1993

188 Notebook, conversation with Emmie Webb 22.3.1986

189 Greeves, 1986, 30

190 Idem

191 Idem

192 Idem

193 *London & West Country Chamber of Mines Records* Vol.I, Part VIII, September 1903, p.178

194 *London & West Country Chamber of Mines Records 1904-1907*, p.73

195 'Tin Mining in Devonshire- Developing the Industry – The Birch Tor Mine', *Devon & Exeter Gazette*, 17 August 1907

196 Greeves, 1986, 23-4

197 Greeves, 1992, 13

198 Greeves, 1986, 31

199 Greeves, 1986, 51

200 Greeves, 1986, 32; oral inf. Frank Warne, tape 30.10.1973

201 Greeves, 1986, 33-34

202 Letter from Donald Smith 8.3.1978

203 Oral inf. Frank Warne, tape 30.10.1973

204 Idem

205 Idem

206 Idem

207 Cornwall Record Office/X91/2/Letters & Reports Relating to Birch Tor & Vitifer Mines, Windeatt & Windeatt to Wilcocks, 2 May 1906, transcribcd by C J Kelland

208 Notebook, conversation with G. Hambley 29.1.1974

209 Greeves, 2011b

210 Notebook, conversation with Mrs Bents 30.10.1973

211 Notebook, conversation with Annie Sleep 24.5.74; oral inf. Reginald Warne, tape 20.5.75; conversation with George Austin 20.10.81; Fernley Warne (Modbury) 11.6.84

212 *Western Morning News* 10 September 1928; Greeves, 1986, 36

213 Greeves, 1986, 36

214 Court, 1927, plate facing p.104, on extreme right of back row

215 Notebook, conversation with Bessie Beer 4.7.1990

216 Greeves, 1986, 38

217 Notebook, conversation with Annie Leaman 27.3.1975

218 Greeves, 1986, 49

219 Notebook, conversations with William Bennett 13.3.1974; Sidney French 7.11.1974

220 Notebook, conversations with Ethel White 30.10.73; John Osborn 22.1.77

221 Notebook, conversation with John Osborn 22.1.1977

222 Notebook, conversations with Amy Osborn 16.9.1969; Blanch & Alfred Wannacott and Ernest Tucker 17.9.1969; George Hellier 7.12.1973

223 Notebook, conversation with Blanch and Alfred Wannacott 17.9.1969

224 Stewart, 2013, 231-2

225 Greeves, 1986, 23

226 Notebook, conversation with Ethel White 30.10.1973

227 Notebook, conversation with Elsie Bellamy 18.7.1976

228 Oral inf. Nellie White, tape 21.6.1972

229 Notebook, conversations with Annie Sleep 9.12.1975; Sidney French 17.12.1975; Elsie Bellamy 18.7.1976

230 Greeves & Stanbrook, 2001

231 Notebook, conversation with Jan Leaman 15.4.1976

232 DuCo London, Mineral Grants Vol.1

233 Greeves, 1985

234 Letter from Bob Cowan to R. Warne 18.7.1998 and 22.7.2012

235 Notebook, conversation with Sidney French 7.11.1974

236 Greeves & Stanbrook, 2001, 23-25

237 Greeves & Stanbrook, 2001, 27

338 Cornwall Record Office/CMDA/1/4/1, transcribed by C J Kelland

239 *Cornish Chamber of Mines Yearbook 1919*, p.17

240 Greeves, 1986, 24

241 Copy of MS in possn Keith Fox

242 *Western Morning News* 4 January 1923

243 DuCo London, Mineral Grants Vol.1

244 Notebook, conversations with Walter Dodd 7.2.1978 and Chris Hill 19.10.1983

245 Greeves, 2011c

246 Greeves, 1986, 45, and note 250 below

247 Newman, 2002, 38-39. A South Stone [i.e. Soussons] Tin Mine is mentioned in 1804, inf. C J Kelland

248 Census 1851

249 Bellamy, 1998, 124

250 *Mining Journal* 10 May 1851 p.223c (copy of text provided by C J Kelland)

251 Greeves, 1986, 45; *Tavistock Gazette* 24 February 1882 (copy ex C J Kelland)

252 Notebook, conversation with Louise Warne 31.8.72; oral inf. Sidney French, tape 4.2.74

253 *Tavistock Gazette* 24 February 1882 (copy ex C J Kelland)

254 Original in possn Graham Amhof

255 Blake, 1915, 342

256 Greeves, 1986, 47

257 Idem

258 Greeves, 1986, 48-9

259 Michelmore, 1946, 27-8

260 The National Archives/IR58/83595/nos 103 & 113 Manaton – ex E Greeves

261 Manaton Census 1911

262 Oral inf. Sidney French, tape 4.2.1974

263 Greeves, 1986, 49

264 Census 1911

265 Bellamy, 1998, 40; Notebook, conversation with Reginald Warne 20.5.75

266 *Western Times*, 26 May 1926

267 Bellamy, 1998, 44

268 Greeves, 1986, 49

269 Idem

270 Notebook, conversation with Elsie Bellamy 18.7.1976

271 Hamilton Jenkin, 1974, 106

272 Notebook, conversation with William Grose 1.8.1981

273 Notebook, conversations with Elsie Bellamy 14.9.1970; Gertrude Prew 9.7.1977

274 Greeves, 1986, 50

275 Oral inf. Donald Smith, tape 16.8.1984

276 Letter from A J Gale 14.5.2001; Bellamy, 1998, 139

277 Letter from A J Gale 14.5.2001

278 Greeves, 1986, 52

279 The National Archives/BT31/12987/ 105975 ex E Stanbrook

280 Richardson, 1992, 112-116

281 Recorded on title page of *Recognition of Minerals* (Mining Journal, 1909)

282 Richardson, 1992, 114-5

283 Notebook, conversation with Elsie Bellamy 18.7.1976

284 Census data supplied by E Greeves

285 Copy of MSS in possn Keith Fox

286 Notebook, conversations with Bill Flewin 1.7.1996 and 3.7.1996; Letter from Justin Brooke 5.7.1996

287 Notebook, conversation with Bill Flewin 1.7.1996

288 Idem

289 Oral inf. Donald Smith, tape 16.8.1984

290 Notebook, conversation with Gilbert Warne 7.9.1971

291 Notebook, conversation with George Austin 20.10.1981

292 Brooks, 2004, 41

293 *Kelly Mine Preservation Society Newsletter*, August 2010, p.4

294 Greeves, 2000b

295 Oral inf. Donald Smith, tape 4.9.1988

296 Oral inf. Donald Smith, tape 16.8.1984

297 Idem

298 Idem

299 Greeves, 1986, 58

300 Notebook, conversations with Donald Smith 26.5.83 and 17.3.92; oral inf. Donald Smith, tape 16.8.84

301 Oral inf. Donald Smith, tape 16.8.1984

302 DuCo London, Mineral Grants Vol.1

303 Notebook, conversation with Deborah Hannaford 18.7.1976

304 Copy of typescript letter 2 October 1927 in author's possn, ex Donald Smith

305 Notebook, conversation with Donald Smith 18.8.1985

306 Notebook, conversation with Donald Smith 17.3.1992

307 Letter from Donald Smith, rec'd 5.11.1983

308 Oral inf. Donald Smith, tape 16.8.1984

309 Idem

310 Notebook, conversations with Gilbert Warne 4.10.83; Donald Smith 24.6.91

311 Oral inf. Donald Smith, tape 4.9.1988

312 Letter from Donald Smith, rec'd 5.11.1983

313 Oral inf. Donald Smith, tape 16.8.1984

314 Idem

315 Idem. A raff wheel raised water or concentrate from one level to another

316 Oral inf. Donald Smith, tape 16.8.1984

317 Devon Heritage Centre/3963M/B3/7; Broughton, 1964

318 Richardson, 1992, 23

319 Notebook, conversation with William John Bowhay 12.3.1984

320 Inf. C J Kelland

321 Notebook, conversations with Jack Hamlyn senior 24.2.84 and Jack Hamlyn junior 16.6.98

322 Notebook, conversation with Donald Smith 26.5.83; oral inf. Donald Smith, tape 16.8.84

323 Notebook, conversation with Donald Smith 26.5.1983

324 Letter from Donald Smith 8.3.1978

325 Notebook, conversation with Donald Smith 17.3.92; oral inf. Donald Smith, tape 16.8.84

326 Oral inf. Donald Smith, tape 16.8.1984

327 Letter from Donald Smith, rec'd 5.11.1983

328 Notebook, conversation with Roy Petherick 25.11.97

329 Oral inf. Donald Smith, tape 16.8.1984

330 Greeves, 1986, 66; notebook, conversation with Frank Williams 4.5.1988

331 Notebook, conversations with Frank Williams 17.8.1986; 31.12.1987; 4.5.1988; 8.11.1989

332 Notebook, conversations with Donald Smith 26.5.83 and 17.3.92

333 Greeves & Stanbrook, 2001, 36-38

334 Notebook, conversation with Donald Smith 26.5.83; Beatie Brook 19.9.2000

335 Greeves & Stanbrook, 2001, 33-34

336 Letter from Donald Smith, rec'd 5.11.1983

337 Idem

338 Notebook, conversations with Beatie Brook 13.12.83 and 19.9.2000

339 Notebook, conversations with Donald Smith 26.5.83 and 17.3.92; for an appreciation of Gilbert Warne see Greeves 2001a

340 Letter from Donald Smith, rec'd 5.11.1983

341 Notebook, conversation with Kenneth Williams 19.6.1986

342 Letter from Donald Smith 5.10.1970; for an appreciation of Donald Smith see Greeves, 1994

343 Oral inf. Donald Smith, tape 4.9.1988

344 Copy of MS handwritten by Stanhope, in possn Keith Fox

345 *Western Morning News* 11 June 1932

346 Notebook, conversation with Keith Fox 18.7.1983

347 Copy of MS in possn Keith Fox

348 Copy of K. Fox MSS, handwritten on 5 sheets of paper, each signed by Mr Vernon Olver

349 Email from John Olver 10.7.2011

350 Inf. Colin Olver, July 2011

351 Copies of MSS in possn Keith Fox

352 Idem

353 Idem

354 Richardson, 1992, 24-5

355 Notebook, conversation with David Hurn 10.1.2000

356 Greeves, 1986, 79

357 DuCo London, Mineral Grants Vol.1

358 Report to The Straits & General Development Co. (1931) Ltd, September 1938 - copy typescript supplied by R. Scrivener, Inst of Geological Sciences, c. 1975

359 Letter from Stanhope to Donald Smith, 8 May 1939

360 Inf. John Olver 2011

361 Notebook, conversation with Irene Bailey 20.11.2001

362 Stevenson Buchan report 21 February 1942 - copy typescript supplied by R. Scrivener c.1975

363 Notebook, conversation with Irene Bailey 20.11.2001; *Western Morning News* 30 December 1942; Western Times 1 January 1943

364 The National Archives/F37/82 – E Greeves notes

BIBLIOGRAPHY

Anon (2014) *Whitehorse Hill – An Early Bronze Age Burial* (Dartmoor National Park Authority, Bovey Tracey)

Bellamy, R. (1998) *Postbridge – The Heart of Dartmoor* (Devon Books/Halsgrove, Tiverton)

Blake, W.J. (1915) 'Hooker's Synopsis Chorographical of Devonshire', *Trans. Devon. Assoc.*, **47**, 334-348

Brooks, T. (2004) *Devon's Last 'Metal' Mine – Great Rock 'Shiny' Ore Mine* (Cornish Hillside Publications, St Austell)

Broughton, D.G. (1964) The Mines of Devon & Dartmoor [typescript, 50pp,incl.plans, in Chagford School]

Broughton, D.G. (1968-9) 'The Birch Tor & Vitifer Tin Mining Complex', *Trans. Cornish Inst. of Engineers*, **24**, 25-49, 50-53

Broughton, D.G. (1971) 'The Land Half Made', K*ingston Geological Review*, Research Seminar Issue, **2** vol.1 no.6, 1-25

Brown, M. (1999) *Dartmoor Field Guides, Vols 1-54* (Dartmoor Press, Plymouth)

Burt, R. *et al* (1984) *Devon and Somerset Mines* (Univ of Exeter)

Court, L.H. (1927) *Some Dartmoor Saints and Shrines* (Morgan & Scott, London)

Falcon, T. (1903) 'Dartmoor Mining', *Devon Notes & Queries*, **2** pt.8, October 1903, 225-227

Greeves, T. (1980) 'A History of Whiteworks Tin Mine, Part One: 1790-1848', *Plymouth Mineral & Mining Club Journal*, **11** no.2, September 1980, 11-16

Greeves, T. (1981) The Devon Tin Industry 1450-1750: An Archaeological & Historical Survey (unpub. PhD thesis, Univ of Exeter)

Greeves, T. (1985) 'Steeperton Tor Tin Mine, Dartmoor, Devon' , *Trans. Devon. Assoc.*, **117**, 101-127

Greeves, T. (1986) *Tin Mines & Miners of Dartmoor: A Photographic Record* (Devon Books, Exeter)

Greeves, T. (1992) 'Adventures with Fiery Dragons – The Cornish Tinner in Devon from the 15th to the 20th century', *Journ. Trevithick Soc.*,**19**, 2-17

Greeves, T. (1994) 'Donald Langley Smith, 22 June 1907-30 June 1993', *Dartmoor Tinworking Research Group Newsletter*, **6**, 14

Greeves, T. (1995) 'William Ambrose Grose 1886-1994', *Dartmoor Tinworking Research Group Newsletter*, **8**, 12

Greeves, T. (2000)a 'Explosives, Gypsies and Strawberries', *Devon Life*, 4/12, June 2000, 46-7

Greeves, T. (2000)b 'An Electric Stove and Ingenuity', *Devon Life*, 5/3, September 2000, 46-7

Greeves, T. (2001)a 'Francis Gilbert ('Gillie') Warne – the Last of the 'Old Men': an Appreciation', *Dartmoor Tinworking Research Group Newsletter*, **20**, January 2001, 5-6

Greeves, T. (2001)b 'William Flewin – A Family Link with Golden Dagger and Birch Tor Mines Eighty Years Ago', *Dartmoor Tinworking Research Group Newsletter*, **21**, Summer 2001, 8-9

Greeves, T. (2002) 'A History of Whiteworks Tin Mine, Part Two: 1848-1914', *Plymouth Mineral & Mining Club Journal*, **32** no.2, October 2002, 1, 3-6

Greeves, T. (2010) 'Historic Mining Image No.1 – Headframe at Low's Shaft, Hexworthy Tin Mine c.1910', *Dartmoor Tinworking Research Group Newsletter*, **38**, January 2010, 10-11

Greeves, T. (2011)a 'Peopling the Mines, Part I – A Preliminary Checklist of Miners and Others at Hexworthy Tin Mine', *Dartmoor Online*, Autumn 2011

Greeves, T. (2011)b 'Nuclear Physics and Dartmoor' – A Visit by Ernest Rutherford in 1911', *Dartmoor Online*, Spring 2011

Greeves, T. (2011)c 'Beatrice Brook (née Warne) 1913-2010 – A last Link with Vitifer & Golden Dagger Tin Mines', *Dartmoor Tinworking Research Group Newsletter*, **40**, January 2011, 4-6

Greeves, T. (2011)d 'Historic Mining Image No.3 – Golden Dagger Tin Mine c.1929 – Moveable Trommels at the lower end of the Redwater valley', *Dartmoor Tinworking Research Group Newsletter*, **40**, January 2011, 17

Greeves, T. (2011)e 'Historic Mining Image No.4 – Hexworthy Mine 1919', *Dartmoor Tinworking Research Group Newsletter*, **41**, July 2011, 11

Greeves, T. (2012)a 'Abandoned Pumping Waterwheel at Wheal Caroline c. 1905 – Historic Mining Image No.5', *Dartmoor Tinworking Research Group Newsletter*, **42**, January 2012, 8

Greeves, T. (2012)b 'Historic Mining Image No.6 – The Dressing Floor at Vitifer Mine c.1900', *Dartmoor Tinworking Research Group Newsletter*, **43**, July 2012, 14

Greeves, T. (2013) 'Historic Mining Image No.7 – Ruined Buildings at Vitifer Mine, April 1937', *Dartmoor Tinworking Research Group Newsletter*, **44**, January 2013, 13

Greeves, T. (2015) *Dartmoor's Earliest Photographs: Landscape & Place 1860-1880* (Twelveheads Press, Truro)

Greeves, T. & Stanbrook, E. (2012) *The Warren House Inn – Dartmoor* (new edn, Bannawell Books, Tavistock)

Hamilton Jenkin, A.K. (1974) *Mines of Devon Volume I: The Southern Area* (David & Charles, Newton Abbot)

Howard, B. (1993) 'Two Gentlemen of Hexworthy', *Dartmoor Tinworking Research Group Newsletter*, **5**, July 1993, 9-10

Macdonald, W. (n.d.) *The Romance of the Golden Rand*

Meharg, A.A., Edwards, K.J., Schofield, J.E. et al (2012) 'First comprehensive peat depositional records for tin, lead and copper associated with the antiquity of Europe's largest cassiterite deposits', *Journal of Archaeological Science*, **39**, 717-727

Michelmore, H.G. (n.d.) [1946] *Fishing Facts and Fancies* (privately publ.)

Milton, P. (2006) *The Discovery of Dartmoor – A Wild and Wondrous Region* (Phillimore, Chichester).

Newman, P. (1996) *Tinworking in the O Brook Valley, Dartmoor, Devonshire* (Royal Commission on the Historical Monuments of England)

Newman, P. (2002) *Headland Warren and the Birch Tor and Vitifer Tin Mines* (English Heritage, Archaeological Investigation Report Series A1/34/2002)

Pryce, W. (1778) *Mineralogia Cornubiensis*

Reid, C. et al (1912) *The Geology of Dartmoor* (HMSO, London)

Richardson, P. (1992) *Mines of Dartmoor and the Tamar Valley after 1913* (British Mining Vol.44, Northern Mine Research Society, Sheffield)

Rowe, S. (1848) *A Perambulation of the Antient and Royal Forest of Dartmoor and the Venville Precincts* (Plymouth)

Stewart, R.J. (2013) *Devon Great Consols – A Mine of Mines* (Trevithick Society)

Thorndycraft, V.R., Pirrie, D. & Brown, A.G. (2004) 'Alluvial Records of Medieval & Prehistoric Tin Mining on Dartmoor, Southwest England', *Geoarchaeology*, **19** no.3, 219-236

Wilson, H. (2015) 'The Grose family of Ilsington', *Dartmoor Tinworking Research Group Newsletter*, **48**, May 2015, 14-17

INDEX

155